AS Music
Listening Tests

Edexcel

Hugh Benham

and

Alistair Wightman

R· RHINEGOLD
EDUCATION

www.r̶ Millennium Centre n.co.uk

First published 2013 in Great Britain by
Rhinegold Education
14–15 Berners Street
London W1T 3LJ
www.rhinegoldeducation.co.uk

© 2013 Rhinegold Education,
a division of Music Sales Limited

You should always check the current requirements of the examination, since these may change.
Copies of the Edexcel specification can be downloaded from the Edexcel website at www.edexcel.com.
Telephone: 01623 467467, Fax: 01623 450481, Email: publication.orders@edexcel.com

Edexcel AS Music Listening Tests
British Library Cataloguing in Publication Data.
A catalogue record for this book is available from the British Library.
Order No. RHG334
ISBN: 978-1-78305-031-4

Exclusive Distributors:
Music Sales Limited
Distribution Centre, Newmarket Road,
Bury St Edmunds, Suffolk, IP33 3YB, UK

Printed in the EU

Contents

The authors

Hugh Benham read Music and English at Southampton University, where he was awarded a PhD for his study of the music of John Taverner. He is a chair of examiners for GCE Music, an in-service trainer, church organist and writer, and formerly taught music in a sixth-form college. Hugh has contributed to *Music Teacher* and *Classroom Music* magazines, and is the author of *Baroque Music in Focus* (Rhinegold, 2nd ed. 2010). His other writing includes two books on English church music, including *John Taverner: his Life and Music* (Ashgate, 2003), articles on early music, contributions to *The New Grove Dictionary of Music and Musicians* (2001) and *Die Musik in Geschichte und Gegenwart*, and a complete edition of Taverner for *Early English Church Music*.

Alistair Wightman read Music at Oxford and then York University, where he was awarded a D. Phil for his study of the music of Karol Szymanowski. He has worked in primary, secondary and further education, and is a freelance teacher and writer as well as principal examiner in history and analysis for A-level music. His publications include *Writing about Music* (Rhinegold, 2008) and several books and articles devoted to Tadeusz Baird, Karłowicz and Szymanowski, including *Karłowicz, Young Poland and the Musical Fin-de-siècle* (Ashgate, 1996), *Karol Szymanowski: his Life and Music* (Ashgate, 1999) and *Szymanowski on Music: Selected Writings of Karol Szymanowski* (Toccata Press, 1999).

Copyright

General introduction

What this book is for

This book will help you to do as well as you possibly can in your Edexcel AS Music Unit 3 exam, focusing in particular on Section A (Listening) and Section C (Understanding Chords and Lines).

The contents of this book

This book begins with tests for Section A (Listening) of the Unit 3 exam. As these tests are based on the set works (which change every year), you need to make sure that you work through the tests **that are related specifically to the year of your AS exam**, either 2014 (pages 9–29) or 2015 (pages 30–61).

This is followed by some brief advice on Section B (Investigating Musical Styles) and a range of practice questions for Section C (Understanding Chords and Lines). The Section C questions are not based on the set works and so are suitable for exams in both 2014 and 2015.

Mark schemes and answers are given at the back of the book, on pages 95–108.

Please note that the Section A and Section C questions in this book first appeared in the second edition (published in 2009), as the 2014–2015 set works are exactly the same as the ones in 2009–2010.

When searching for practice questions for Unit 3 you are not limited to the tests in this book: see the section 'How to find and invent more questions for Unit 3' on pages 92–94.

Recordings

The recordings that you need to listen to when answering the Section A tests can be found on the CDs that accompany the Edexcel A level *Anthology of Music*. Each Section A test tells you which of the Edexcel CDs to use, which track, and which part of that track.

You are free to use recordings other than those from the Edexcel CDs, but you should be aware that you may encounter difficulties, not just with timings but with discrepancies arising from details of performance, such as tempi, balance and the like.

How to use this book

When working through the Section A tests in this book, you might want to keep to exam conditions as closely as possible: listen to the excerpt five times only – with short pauses in-between each playing (see page 9) – and answer the questions by yourself. But you could also use the tests in a more relaxed manner, as practice and learning materials rather than pretend exam questions – for example, by listening to each excerpt as many times as you need and consulting with others in order to work out the right answers. You could also try working through some of the tests a second time after you have had a chance to forget your answers.

The same applies to Section C: to begin with, you might want to take as long as you like to answer the questions, but later on it would be wise to consider how much time will actually be available in the exam itself.

How to do as well as you possibly can in the exam

1. **Read each question** – all of it – thoroughly and do exactly what it asks. You will have time to look at the questions before the exam begins. Because the music will be from set works that you should know well, you will probably be able to spot one or two answers before the music is played – but always check any such predicted answers carefully when you do hear the music.

2. **Don't panic.** Prepare thoroughly, and this should give you the confidence to do your best.

3. **Concentrate.** There is no time to let your attention wander, especially in Section A, where there can be ten or more parts to each question, and only five chances to hear the music.

4. **Manage your time carefully.** In particular, don't get bogged down with questions whose answers you really don't know or can't remember.

5. **Make sufficient points** to gain the number of marks available. Take note of the bracketed sub-totals after questions. For example, '(3)' means 'three marks': to get all of these you will need to make three valid points. Let's imagine that two marks are available for a question whose answer you decide is 'a sequence'. That alone (if correct) will get one mark. Consider what else might be needed to gain the second mark – for example, is it a *rising* sequence or a *falling* sequence?

6. **Lots of words don't always earn lots of marks.** Be as concise as reasonably possible, and always **relevant**. If a question is about texture and you write about tonality, you won't get any marks, however true your comments might be – you will just have wasted valuable time. But it is only common sense to use a whole phrase or sentence to explain a point if you can't think of the right technical words in the heat of the moment. Nevertheless…

7. **Whenever you can, use the accepted technical words** (imitation, sequence and so on). Remember also: the questions themselves often use such technical words – so if you don't understand them, you won't be able to answer correctly.

If you come across technical words that you don't understand when working through the tests in this book, consult the glossary at the back (pages 109–112) or a dictionary such as the *Dictionary of Music in Sound* by David Bowman (Rhinegold Education, 2002).

Introduction to Section A (Listening)

The Unit 3 exam begins with listening questions based on two of the set works you have studied from the Edexcel *Anthology of Music*.

> The set works for 2014 and 2015 are listed in the Edexcel specification on pages 58–59.

Questions and part-questions

Question 1 in your exam will be based on an excerpt from one of the set works in the **Instrumental Music** area of study. Question 2 will be based on an excerpt from a set work in the **Vocal Music** area of study.

You won't know which works will feature in these questions until you open your exam paper, so you must study every work with equal care.

Each listening question will have a number of parts, labelled alphabetically. You must answer all of them. One or more parts will be multiple choice, and for these you have to answer by putting a cross in a box. Some other parts will require one- or two-word answers, phrases or whole sentences. After each part you'll see in brackets how many marks it is worth: where two or more marks are available, you are expected to make the same number of valid points.

In Section A answers you can use continuous prose where appropriate, but it's not necessary. You will not be marked on quality of written communication, as in Section B answers, but you should still aim to get spellings right (especially words frequently misspelt such as 'bass' and 'rhythm').

Most parts of a listening question will relate to just a few bars (starting at or near the beginning and then working through the passage). There may also be one or more general parts. These may require some knowledge of the whole piece from which the excerpt is taken – for instance, you may have to recognise which part of the piece the excerpt comes from.

In this book we have mainly chosen excerpts that do not come from the beginning of a piece. This is to remind you that examiners are free to do this, and to help you get used to the fact that in such cases the numbering of bars in the skeleton score will always start at 1, wherever the passage comes from in a set work.

Listening to the excerpts

In the exam, the music for each question will be played to you five times. There will be timed pauses between each playing and after the final playing, to allow you to write your answers. The lengths of the pauses will be announced so you know how much time you have to write – they will vary between 30 seconds and 3 minutes in length (see page 9).

When you work through the tests from this book, you must supply your own recordings, as explained above (see page 5). You will have to time the pauses yourself, or ask someone else to help you, in accordance with the instructions on page 9.

Skeleton scores in the exam

You won't have a complete copy of the Anthology in the exam, but a separate booklet will contain 'skeleton scores' of the two excerpts you will hear. Each skeleton score will provide you with outline musical notation, on a single stave (or possibly on two staves, according to Edexcel's online tutor support materials). The skeleton score will probably have the principal melodic line at least some of the time. Elsewhere it may show the bass line, or may just provide the rhythm. Exactly what you're given will depend on what you're asked about: it's very unlikely that the pitches of the melodic line for bars 5–8 will be printed if you have to recognise a melodic sequence in these bars, for example.

Each skeleton score will have bar numbers. If an excerpt is taken from the start of a set work, the bar numbers of the skeleton score will be the same as those of the Anthology. Where an excerpt comes from later in a work, the bar numbers of the skeleton score will be numbered from 1 onwards, so they won't in this case match the numbering of the Anthology. When you answer about details of melody, chords and texture, this is no problem: you're hardly likely to have learned each set work literally bar-by-bar. It does mean, however, that if you're asked about where an excerpt comes within the whole piece, you will need to rely on the *sound* of the music, not just on remembering (for example) that this must be the development section because it's labelled bar 80.

Skeleton scores will have 'cues' to help you. For example, if you are asked to identify the key and cadence at a particular point, the words 'Key and cadence?' are likely to appear on the skeleton score in the appropriate bar(s).

During the exam, remember to:

1. **Read the questions** during the time allowed for this before the music is played for the first time. If you think you already know any answers, jot them down at this point: confirm (or change) them later.

2. **Read every part of each question thoroughly.** Do exactly what it tells you.

3. **Note how many marks are awarded for each part.** Don't get bogged down with a hard one-mark question. With questions worth two or more marks, try to make enough points to qualify for all the marks available.

4. **Keep calm.** It's possible to get flustered when you first see a question, with all its various parts. But remember:

   ➢ There are always at least one or two quite easy bits
   ➢ Some, if not many or most, of the answers may come to you during or after the third, fourth and fifth playings. Don't panic if, early on, your paper has a lot of blank spaces.

Section A (Listening)

When working through the listening tests that follow, you will need a copy of the CDs that accompany the Edexcel *Anthology of Music*. For each test, you are told which CD to use, which track, and which part of that track. In the early stages, you can listen to each excerpt as many times as you like, and need not time the pauses between listenings. But when practising for the exam, give yourself a minute or two to read the questions, and then follow the procedure shown below (or ask someone else to operate the CD player and time the pauses):

➢ Play the music for the first time, followed by a 30-second pause
➢ Play the music for the second time, followed by a 1-minute pause
➢ Play the music for the third time, followed by a 1-minute pause
➢ Play the music for the fourth time, followed by a 30-second pause
➢ Play the music for the fifth and final time, followed by a 3-minute pause, during which you should finish your answers.

Tests for 2014

You will find 10 tests below based on the set works for 2014. Tests on Instrumental Music and Vocal Music are presented as one mixed group rather than as two separate groups, to encourage you to practise both areas of study equally.

For finding and inventing additional Section A questions, see pages 92–94.

2014 Test 1

CD 1 Track 2, 0:00–1:00

You will hear an excerpt from the first movement of Symphony No. 26 in D minor ('Lamentatione') by Haydn. A skeleton score of this excerpt is provided below. Bar numbers in this question refer to the skeleton score.

(a) Name the instruments playing the part given in the skeleton score at bars 1 to 8.

....

(1)

Note carefully the *octave* of the printed part. Other instruments play a similar part an octave lower.

(b) Two ornament symbols have been omitted from bar 10. Insert them in the stave below:

(2)

(c) Name the type of dissonance heard at the beginning of bar 16.

....

(1)

Hint: Is the first note of bar 16 approached by step, by leap, or prolonged from the bar before?

(d) Describe the first-violin part at bars 26 to 29. (The printed part is played by second violins and oboes.)

....

....

.... *(3)*

(e) Comment on the melody played by second violins and oboes at bars 32 to 34.

....

.... *(2)*

(f) Name the key and cadence at bars 40 to 41.

Key .... Cadence .... *(2)*

(g) Comment on the instrumentation and texture in bars 43 to 44.

....

....

.... *(3)*

(h) Put a cross in the box next to the statement that is true.

☐ **A** The melody in bars 17–39 is adapted from folksong

☐ **B** The melody in bars 17–39 is adapted from plainsong

☐ **C** The melody in bars 17–39 is adapted from a chorale

☐ **D** The melody in bars 17–39 is adapted from a lied *(1)*

Exam tests may well include a multiple-choice question such as this, perhaps applying to the entire excerpt and requiring you to demonstrate knowledge previously learnt, as well as testing listening skills.

(i) Put a cross in the box next to the statement that is true.

☐ **A** This excerpt is the whole exposition section

☐ **B** This excerpt is the whole development section

☐ **C** This excerpt is the whole recapitulation section

☐ **D** This excerpt is the whole coda section *(1)*

(Total 16 marks)

2014 Test 2   **CD 3 Track 9, 0:32–2:09**

You will hear an excerpt from the third movement of *Symphony of Psalms* by Stravinsky. A skeleton score of this excerpt is provided below. Bar numbers in this question refer to the skeleton score.

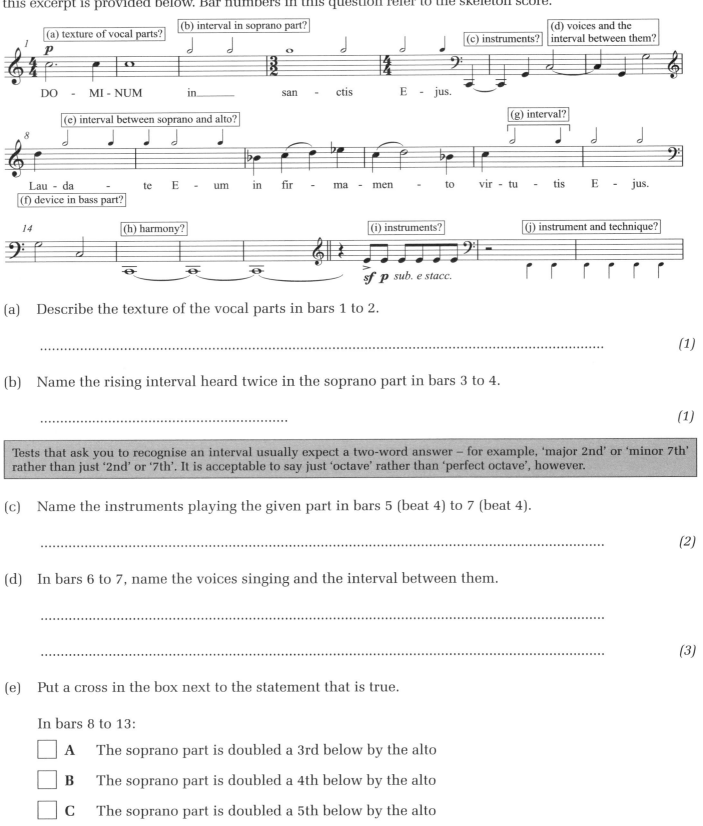

(a)   Describe the texture of the vocal parts in bars 1 to 2.

....   *(1)*

(b)   Name the rising interval heard twice in the soprano part in bars 3 to 4.

....   *(1)*

Tests that ask you to recognise an interval usually expect a two-word answer – for example, 'major 2nd' or 'minor 7th' rather than just '2nd' or '7th'. It is acceptable to say just 'octave' rather than 'perfect octave', however.

(c)   Name the instruments playing the given part in bars 5 (beat 4) to 7 (beat 4).

....   *(2)*

(d)   In bars 6 to 7, name the voices singing and the interval between them.

....

....   *(3)*

(e)   Put a cross in the box next to the statement that is true.

       In bars 8 to 13:

       ☐   A   The soprano part is doubled a 3rd below by the alto

       ☐   B   The soprano part is doubled a 4th below by the alto

       ☐   C   The soprano part is doubled a 5th below by the alto

       ☐   D   The soprano part is doubled a 6th below by the alto   *(1)*

(f)   What compositional device is used in the bass parts in bars 8 to 13?

....   *(1)*

(g)   In bar 12, name the interval between the second and third notes of the soprano part.

....   *(1)*

(h)   Describe the harmony in bars 15 to 17.

....

....   *(2)*

Questions on harmony may require you to identify chords in terms of Roman numerals (I, IV, Vb etc.) or chord symbols (Gm, F⁷ etc.), or may be more open (as here). More 'open' harmony questions may expect, for example, references to *types* of chords, or to chord progressions, or to special harmonic features (such as false relation or tierce de Picardie).

(i)   Which instruments play the quaver motif in bar 18?

....   *(2)*

(j)   Name the instrument playing the bass part of bars 19 to 20, and give the term for the playing technique used here.

....   *(2)*

(Total 16 marks)

CD 2 Track 7, 0:00–1:07

You will hear an excerpt from the third movement of the Piano Quintet in F minor, Op. 34 by Brahms. A skeleton score of this excerpt is provided below. Bar numbers in this question refer to the skeleton score.

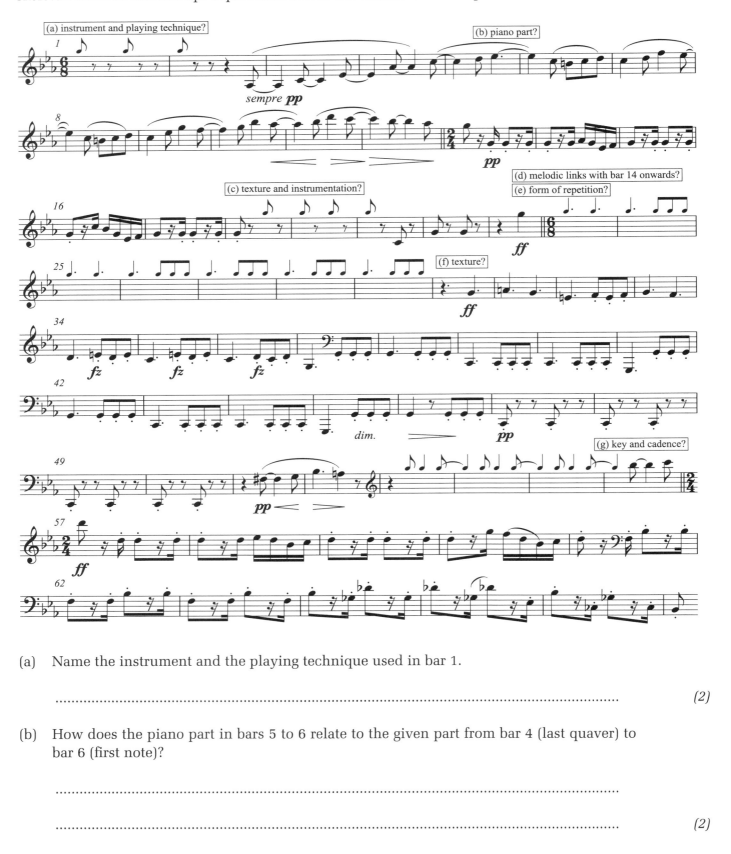

(a) Name the instrument and the playing technique used in bar 1.

....   *(2)*

(b) How does the piano part in bars 5 to 6 relate to the given part from bar 4 (last quaver) to bar 6 (first note)?

....

....   *(2)*

(c)   Comment on the texture and instrumentation in bars 18 to 20.

....

....   *(2)*

(d)   How does the melodic line of bars 22 to 25 relate to that of the section that begins at bar 14?

....

....   *(2)*

(e)   What form of repetition is used in bars 22 to 26?

....   *(1)*

(f)   Comment on the texture in bars 30 to 34.

....

....

....   *(3)*

Some texture questions require a single word or phrase (such as 'monophonic', 'homophonic', 'contrapuntal', 'octaves'). The present three-mark question is one that requires more detail. Start by listening to what the strings do.

(g)   Name the key and cadence at bars 56 to 57.

Key ....   Cadence ....   *(2)*

(h)   Put a cross in the box next to the statement that is true.

☐   **A**   The tempo marking for this excerpt is Allegro

☐   **B**   The tempo marking for this excerpt is Andante

☐   **C**   The tempo marking for this excerpt is Moderato

☐   **D**   The tempo marking for this excerpt is Presto   *(1)*

(i)   Put a cross in the box next to the statement that is true.

☐   **A**   The excerpt is the opening of the scherzo

☐   **B**   The excerpt is the fugato section in the middle of the scherzo

☐   **C**   The excerpt is the trio section

☐   **D**   The excerpt is the ending of the movement   *(1)*

(Total 16 marks)

2014 Test 4

You will hear an excerpt from 'You Can Get It If You Really Want' by Jimmy Cliff (recorded by Desmond Dekker and The Aces). A skeleton score of this excerpt is provided below. Bar numbers in this question refer to the skeleton score.

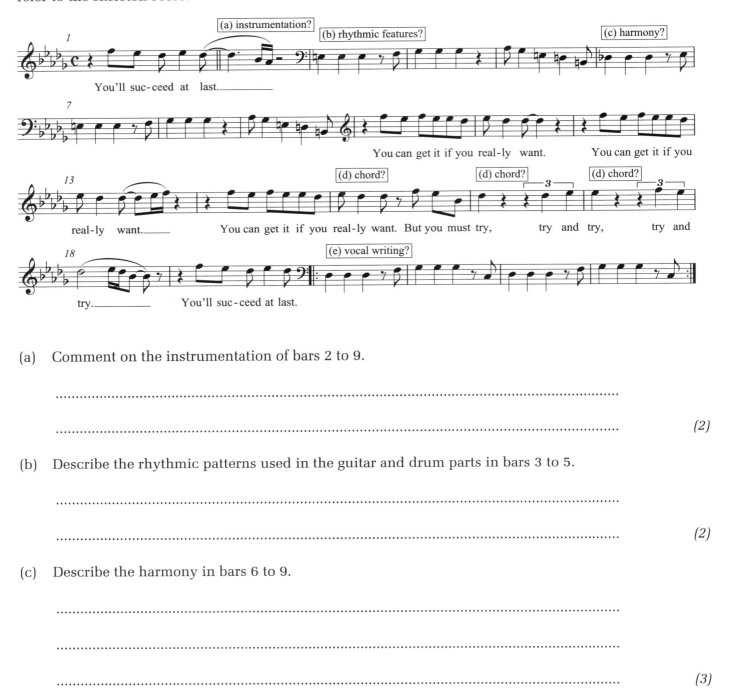

(a) Comment on the instrumentation of bars 2 to 9.

....

.... *(2)*

(b) Describe the rhythmic patterns used in the guitar and drum parts in bars 3 to 5.

....

.... *(2)*

(c) Describe the harmony in bars 6 to 9.

....

....

.... *(3)*

(d) Complete the following table of chords.

Bar 14	D♭
Bar 15	
Bar 16	
Bar 17	

(3)

(e) Comment on the writing for lead and backing vocals in bars 20 to 23.

....

....

....

(3)

Remember that when examiners use the word 'comment', they are hoping that you will say not just what happens but will remark on how it is unusual, important, etc.

(f) Give a single word to describe the texture of this excerpt.

....

(1)

(g) Put a cross in the box next to the statement that is most accurate.

☐ **A** The lead vocal line in this excerpt draws on the major scale

☐ **B** The lead vocal line in this excerpt draws on the minor scale

☐ **C** The lead vocal line in this excerpt draws on the pentatonic scale

☐ **D** The lead vocal line in this excerpt draws on the whole-tone scale

(1)

(h) Put a cross in the box next to the statement that is true.

☐ **A** This excerpt starts with the end of a verse

☐ **B** This excerpt starts with the introduction

☐ **C** This excerpt starts with the end of the chorus

☐ **D** This excerpt starts with a turnaround

(1)

(Total 16 marks)

2014 Test 5   **CD 2 Track 16, 0:34–1:53**

You will hear an excerpt from the Sarabande from *Pour le piano* by Debussy. A skeleton score of this excerpt is provided below. Bar numbers in this question refer to the skeleton score.

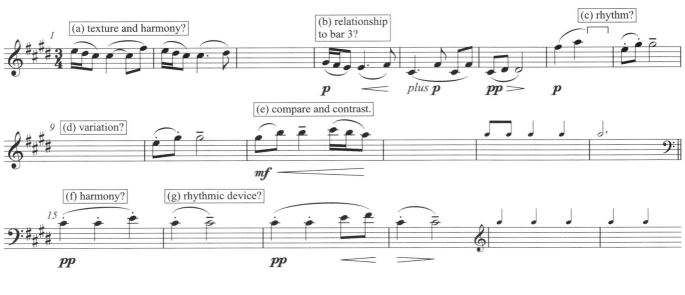

(a)   Describe the texture and harmony in bars 1 to 4.

....

....

....

....   *(4)*

> Note that bars 3, 9 and 12 of the skeleton score are blank. This doesn't mean that there is silence in these bars, but simply that notation for these bars is withheld because it might give away some of the answers required.

> Perhaps it's a bit daunting to be faced with a four-mark question at the start of a test, but there's a lot you can say, as both texture and harmony are covered. Perhaps begin with a single-word description of texture ... to which you can then add a little detail.

(b)   How does the music of bar 4 relate to the music of bar 3?

....   *(1)*

(c)   Describe the rhythm at the third beat of bar 7.

....   *(1)*

(d)   How is the melody line of bar 7 varied in bar 9?

....   *(1)*

(e)   Compare and contrast bars 11 and 12.

....

....

....   *(4)*

(f)   Comment on the harmony in bars 15 to 20.

....

....

....   *(3)*

(g)   Name the rhythmic device used in bar 16.

....   *(1)*

(h)   Put a cross in the box next to the term that best describes the harmony of the excerpt.

☐ **A**   Atonal

☐ **B**   Chromatic

☐ **C**   Functional

☐ **D**   Non-functional   *(1)*

(Total 16 marks)

2014 Test 6   **CD 3 Track 12, 0:23–1:06 (starting at the *repeat* of the opening music)**

You will hear an excerpt from 'Sing we at pleasure' by Weelkes. A skeleton score of this excerpt is provided below. Bar numbers in this question refer to the skeleton score.

We haven't provided any more 'helpful hints' with this test or in Tests 7–10, as you need to get used to managing without them as you prepare for the exam.

(a)   In bar 2, a second soprano part enters. How does it relate to the printed first soprano line in bar 1?

....   *(1)*

(b)   How much lower is the phrase that begins at bar 13, beat 3 than the previous phrase in the printed part? Name the interval.

....   *(1)*

(c)   Name the rhythmic device used in bars 20 to 21.

....   *(1)*

(d)   Name the key at bars 24 to 25 (beat 2).

....   *(1)*

(e)   In bars 26 to 29, how does the second soprano part relate to the printed first soprano part?

....

....   *(2)*

(f)   Identify the type of texture used in bars 31 to 33.

....   *(1)*

(g)   Comment on the writing for voices in bars 34 to 42.

....

....

....

....   *(4)*

(h)   Complete the following table of chords.

Bar 41 (beat 3)	G major in first inversion
Bar 42 (beat 1)	
Bar 42 (beat 3)	
Bar 43 (beat 1)	

(3)

(i)   Put a cross in the box next to the statement that best describes the music you have heard.

☐ **A**   This excerpt is taken from a ballad

☐ **B**   This excerpt is taken from a ballett

☐ **C**   This excerpt is taken from a galliard

☐ **D**   This excerpt is taken from a lied   *(1)*

(j)   Put a cross in the box next to the term that best describes the structure of the music from which the excerpt is taken.

☐ **A**   Binary

☐ **B**   Strophic

☐ **C**   Through-composed

☐ **D**   Tripartite   *(1)*

(Total 16 marks)

2014 Test 7   **CD 1 Track 2, 1:57–2:52**

You will hear an excerpt from the first movement of Symphony No. 26 in D Minor ('Lamentatione'), Op. 26 by Haydn. A skeleton score of this excerpt is provided below. Bar numbers in this question refer to the skeleton score.

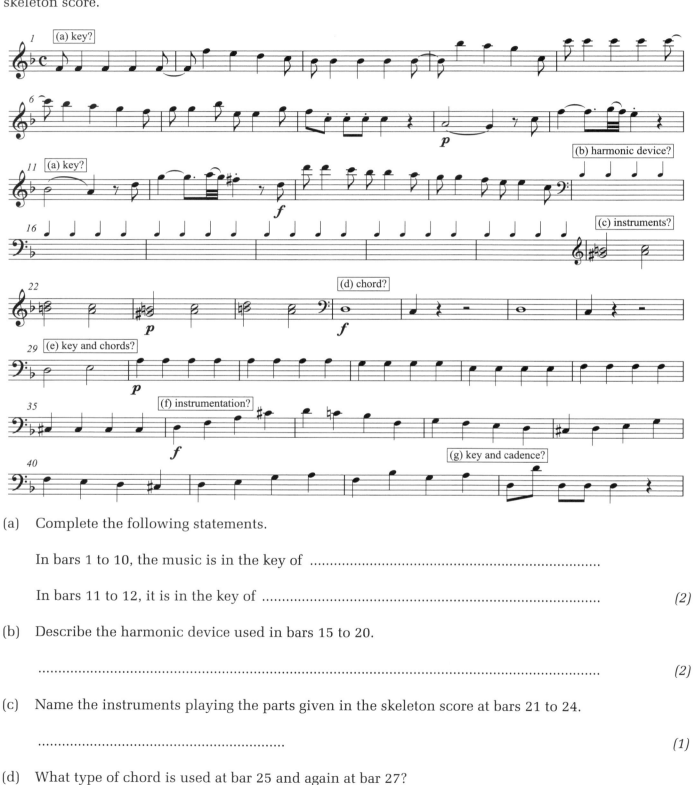

(a)   Complete the following statements.

      In bars 1 to 10, the music is in the key of ....

      In bars 11 to 12, it is in the key of ....   *(2)*

(b)   Describe the harmonic device used in bars 15 to 20.

      ....   *(2)*

(c)   Name the instruments playing the parts given in the skeleton score at bars 21 to 24.

      ....   *(1)*

(d)   What type of chord is used at bar 25 and again at bar 27?

      ....   *(1)*

(e)   Complete the following statements.

At bars 29 to 30 the music is in the key of ....

The chord on the third crotchet beat of bar 29 is ....

The chord on the fourth crotchet beat of bar 29 is ....   *(3)*

(f)   Comment on the instrumentation of bars 36 to 39.

....

....

....   *(3)*

(g)   Name the key and cadence at bars 42 to 43.

Key ....   Cadence ....   *(2)*

(h)   Put a cross in the box next to the statement that is true.

The overall structure of the piece from which this excerpt is taken is:

☐ **A**   Ternary form

☐ **B**   Rondo form

☐ **C**   Sonata form

☐ **D**   Theme and variations   *(1)*

(i)   Put a cross in the box next to the statement that is true.

☐ **A**   This excerpt comes from a Baroque work

☐ **B**   This excerpt comes from an early Classical work

☐ **C**   This excerpt comes from a late Classical work

☐ **D**   This excerpt comes from an early Romantic work   *(1)*

(Total 16 marks)

2014 Test 8   **CD 4 Track 10, 1:20–2:13**

You will hear an excerpt from 'I'm Leavin' You' by Howlin' Wolf. A skeleton score of this excerpt is provided below. Bar numbers in this question refer to the skeleton score.

(a)   Describe the vocal style used in bars 3 and 5.

       ....   *(1)*

(b)   Name the instrument playing the printed part in bar 4.

       ....   *(1)*

(c)   Some 'blue-note' accidentals have been omitted from the given part of bar 6. Insert them
       at the appropriate places on the stave below.

                                                                                            (2)

(d)   Name the instrument playing the rhythm shown above the stave in bars 11 to 12.

       ....   *(1)*

(e) Describe the instrumental techniques employed in the printed part in bars 11 to 12.

....

.... *(2)*

(f) Describe the roles of the voice and of the instruments in bars 15 to 18.

....

....

.... *(3)*

(g) Complete the following table of chords.

Bar 17	G
Bar 19	
Bar 21	
Bar 23	

(3)

(h) Describe the way the quavers in the printed part in bar 25 are performed rhythmically.

.... *(1)*

(i) Put a cross in the box next to the statement that is true.

☐ **A** This excerpt is taken from an example of reggae

☐ **B** This excerpt is taken from an example of rhythm and blues

☐ **C** This excerpt is taken from an example of rocksteady

☐ **D** This excerpt is taken from an example of electric folk *(1)*

(j) Put a cross in the box next to the statement that is true.

☐ **A** The overall structure of the song from which this excerpt is taken is binary

☐ **B** The overall structure of the song from which this excerpt is taken is ternary

☐ **C** The overall structure of the song from which this excerpt is taken is strophic

☐ **D** The overall structure of the song from which this excerpt is taken is 16-bar popular song form *(1)*

(Total 16 marks)

2014 Test 9   **CD 2 Track 7, 1:07–1:56**

You will hear an excerpt from the third movement of the Piano Quintet in F minor, Op. 34 by Brahms. A skeleton score of this excerpt is provided below. Bar numbers in this question refer to the skeleton score.

(a)   Put a cross in the box next to the term that best describes the opening passage.

☐   **A**   Antiphony

☐   **B**   Canon

☐   **C**   Fugato

☐   **D**   Imitation   *(1)*

(b)   Is the key major or minor in bars 1 to 3 (first quaver beat)?

....   *(1)*

(c)   Name the instrument playing the printed melody in bars 1 to 4.

....   *(1)*

(d) How does Brahms treat this melody in bars 5 to 8?

....

.... *(2)*

(e) Name the instrument playing the given rhythm in bars 14 to 17.

.... *(1)*

(f) Name a compositional device used in bars 26 to 28.

.... *(2)*

(g) Comment on Brahms' melodic writing in bars 28 to 33.

....

....

.... *(3)*

(h) Describe the texture in bars 39 to 42, and the role of the instruments in it.

....

....

.... *(3)*

(i) Complete the following sentences.

The cadence in bars 41 to 42 is ....

The key of bars 43 to 49 is .... *(2)*

(Total 16 marks)

2014 Test 10  **CD 3 Track 9, 5:51–7:23**

You will hear an excerpt from the third movement of *Symphony of Psalms* by Stravinsky. A skeleton score of this excerpt is provided below. Bar numbers in this question refer to the skeleton score.

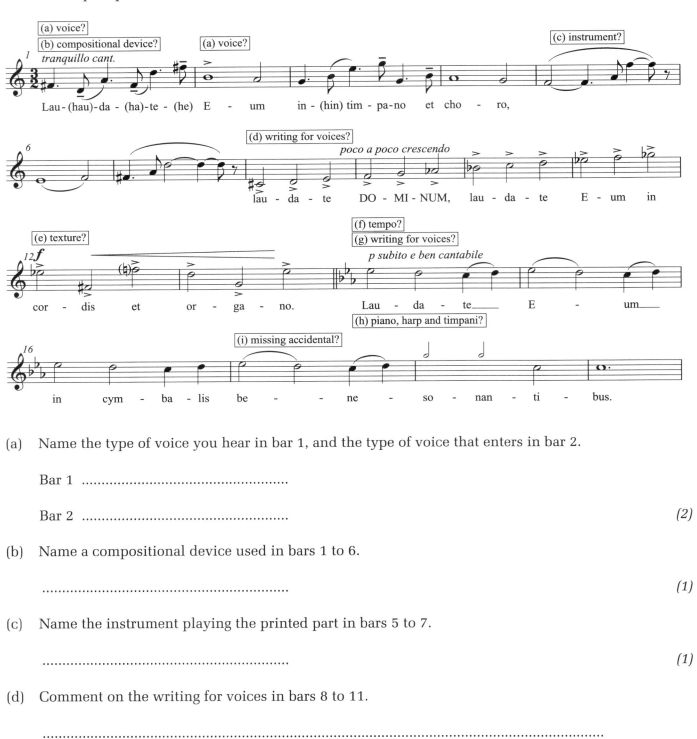

(a) Name the type of voice you hear in bar 1, and the type of voice that enters in bar 2.

Bar 1 ....

Bar 2 .... *(2)*

(b) Name a compositional device used in bars 1 to 6.

.... *(1)*

(c) Name the instrument playing the printed part in bars 5 to 7.

.... *(1)*

(d) Comment on the writing for voices in bars 8 to 11.

....

....

.... *(3)*

(e) Describe the texture in bars 12 to 13.

.... *(1)*

(f) Is the passage starting in bar 14 faster, slower or at the same tempo as the preceding section?

.... *(1)*

(g) Comment on the writing for voices in bars 14 to 19.

....

....

.... *(3)*

(h) Comment on the rhythm and melody of the line played by piano, harp and timpani in bars 14 to 19.

....

....

.... *(3)*

(i) An accidental has been omitted from bar 17. Insert it at the appropriate point on the stave below.

in   cym - ba - lis   be   -   ne -   *(1)*

(Total 16 marks)

Tests for 2015

You will find 16 tests below based on the set works for 2015. Some of the longer works have two tests each, while the shorter ones just have one test. Tests on Instrumental Music and Vocal Music are presented as one mixed group rather than as two separate groups, to encourage you to practise both areas of study equally.

> Before you start, remember *the* most vital piece of advice: answer the question. In particular, when examiners use the word 'comment', they are hoping that you will say not just what happens but will remark on how it is unusual, important, etc.

2015 Test 1   CD 1 Track 1, 0:00–0:59

You will hear an excerpt from the first movement of Brandenburg Concerto No. 4 in G by J. S. Bach. A skeleton score of this excerpt is provided below. Bar numbers in this question refer to the skeleton score.

(a)   Name the instrument playing the part in bars 1 to 6 of the skeleton score.

       ....   *(1)*

(b)   In bars 7 to 9, the key is G major. Name the chords used in:

       Bar 7 .... Bar 8 .... Bar 9 .... *(3)*

> Listening tests sometimes require you to identify particular chords. If the music is in the classical tradition, it is best to use Roman numerals (I, IV, Vb, etc.). *Hint:* Make sure that your answer is harmonically possible in terms of the notes given in the skeleton score (chord V would *not* fit the G in bar 7, for example).

(c)   Name the compositional device used in bars 15 to 18.

       ....   *(1)*

(d)   What is the key of the music in bars 20 to 25? How does this key relate to the tonic key of the movement?

       ....   *(2)*

(e)   Comment on the instrumentation and texture of bars 30 to 34.

       ....

       ....   *(3)*

(f)   Put a cross in the box next to the statement that is true.

    ☐ **A**   The melody in bars 35 to 36 of the skeleton score is doubled a 3rd higher

    ☐ **B**   The melody in bars 35 to 36 of the skeleton score is doubled a 6th higher

    ☐ **C**   The melody in bars 35 to 36 of the skeleton score is doubled a 3rd lower

    ☐ **D**   The melody in bars 35 to 36 of the skeleton score is doubled a 6th lower   *(1)*

(g)   What is the key of the music in bars 40 to 43? How does this key relate to the tonic key of the movement?

       ....   *(2)*

(h)   Name two compositional devices used in bars 43 to 46.

       ....   *(2)*

> 'Compositional devices' are widely used, standard 'tricks of the trade' that composers use to develop musical ideas and/or to create interest and variety. Commonly used 'devices' include simple repetition, sequence, imitation and syncopation.

(i)   Put a cross in the box next to the statement that is true.

       The overall structure of the piece from which this excerpt is taken is:

    ☐ **A**   Ternary form

    ☐ **B**   Sonata form

    ☐ **C**   Ritornello form

    ☐ **D**   Rondo form   *(1)*

> Exam tests may well include a multiple-choice question such as this one, where you have to rely on your previous knowledge about the set work (rather than your listening skills).

(Total 16 marks)

2015 Test 2   **CD 3 Track 13, 0:00–1:10**

You will hear an excerpt from 'Ohimè, se tanto amate' by Monteverdi. A skeleton score of this excerpt is provided below. Bar numbers in this question refer to the skeleton score.

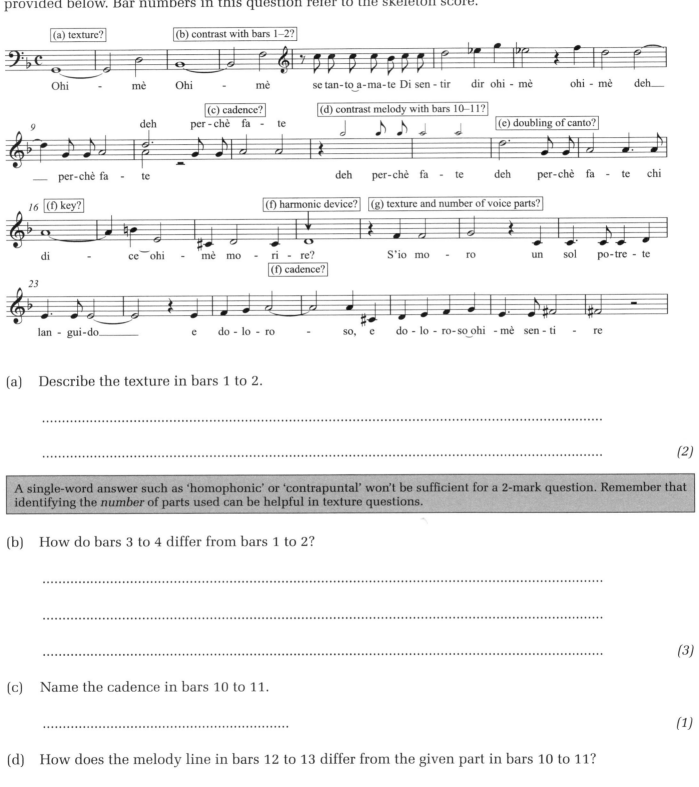

(a) Describe the texture in bars 1 to 2.

....

.... *(2)*

> A single-word answer such as 'homophonic' or 'contrapuntal' won't be sufficient for a 2-mark question. Remember that identifying the *number* of parts used can be helpful in texture questions.

(b) How do bars 3 to 4 differ from bars 1 to 2?

....

....

.... *(3)*

(c) Name the cadence in bars 10 to 11.

.... *(1)*

(d) How does the melody line in bars 12 to 13 differ from the given part in bars 10 to 11?

....

.... *(2)*

(e) Put a cross in the box next to the statement that is true.

The given part (canto) in bars 14 to 15 is doubled by the other soprano part (quinto) a:

☐ **A**   3rd below

☐ **B**   3rd above

☐ **C**   6th below

☐ **D**   6th above   *(1)*

(f) Complete the following statements.

The key of the music in bars 16 to 19 is ....

The cadence in bars 18 to 19 is ...., and the

harmonic device used on the last chord is a .... *(3)*

(g) Name the type of texture in bars 20 to 21, and identify the number of voice parts heard.

.... *(2)*

(h) In what bar do you hear all five voices singing together for the **first** time?

.... *(1)*

This question, unlike most others, is neither focused on a specific short passage, nor something very general like (i) below that you're likely to remember from previous study. When the full five-part choir sings, you should be conscious of greater weight, density and richness than elsewhere.

(i) Put a cross in the box next to the statement that is true.

☐ **A**   This excerpt is taken from an anthem

☐ **B**   This excerpt is taken from a madrigal

☐ **C**   This excerpt is taken from a cantata

☐ **D**   This excerpt is taken from an opera   *(1)*

(Total 16 marks)

2015 Test 3   **CD 1 Track 11, 0:00–1:07**

You will hear an excerpt from the first movement of String Quartet No. 8, Op. 110 by Shostakovich. A skeleton score of this excerpt is provided below. Bar numbers in this question refer to the skeleton score.

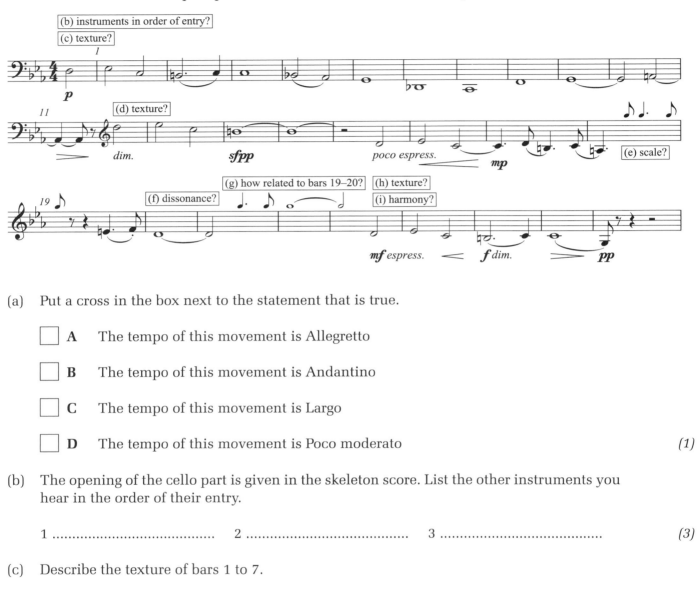

(a) Put a cross in the box next to the statement that is true.

☐ A   The tempo of this movement is Allegretto

☐ B   The tempo of this movement is Andantino

☐ C   The tempo of this movement is Largo

☐ D   The tempo of this movement is Poco moderato   *(1)*

(b) The opening of the cello part is given in the skeleton score. List the other instruments you hear in the order of their entry.

1 ....   2 ....   3 ....   *(3)*

(c) Describe the texture of bars 1 to 7.

....   *(1)*

(d) Comment on the texture from bar 11 (third crotchet beat) to bar 13 (second crotchet beat).

....

....   *(2)*

(e) Name the type of scale used in the part indicated by the notes above the stave in bars 18 to 19.

....   *(1)*

(f)   What type of dissonance is used on the first beat of bar 20?

....   *(1)*

(g)   How do bars 21 to 22 relate to bars 19 to 20?

....   *(1)*

(h)   What one word best describes the texture at bars 23 (beat 3) to 24?

....   *(1)*

(i)   Comment on the harmony from bar 23 (beat 3) to the end of the excerpt.

....

....

....   *(4)*

> The word 'comment' gives you the opportunity to remark on features which are unusual, important, etc., as well as identifying any chords that you recognise. For example, what is noteworthy about the final chord?

(j)   From which of his symphonies does Shostakovich quote in this excerpt?

....   *(1)*

(Total 16 marks)

2015 Test 4   CD 3 Track 17, 0:00–1:06

You will hear an excerpt from 'Après un rêve' by Fauré. A skeleton score of this excerpt is provided below. Bar numbers in this question refer to the skeleton score.

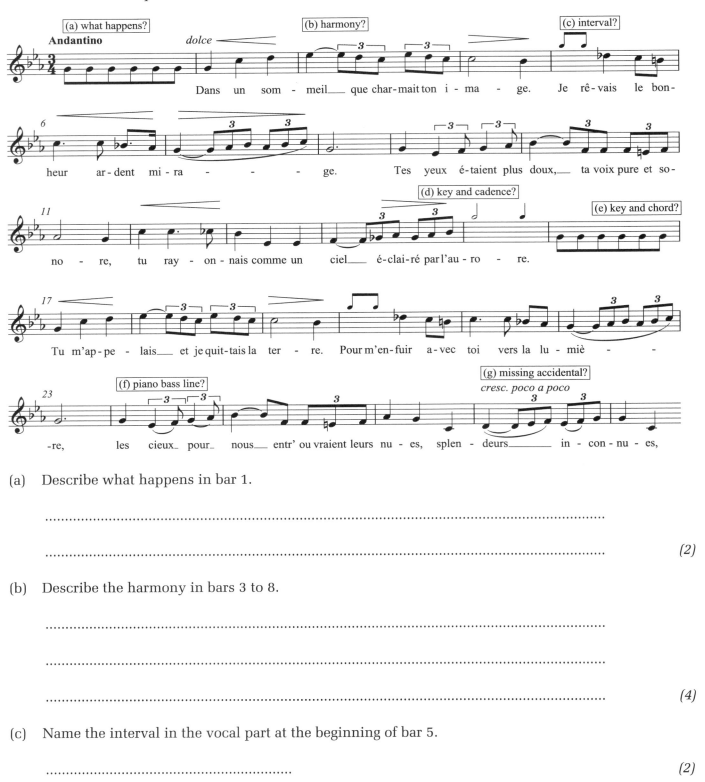

(a)   Describe what happens in bar 1.

       ....

       ....   *(2)*

(b)   Describe the harmony in bars 3 to 8.

       ....

       ....

       ....   *(4)*

(c)   Name the interval in the vocal part at the beginning of bar 5.

       ....   *(2)*

> Questions about intervals usually expect a two-word answer – for example, 'major 2nd' or 'minor 7th' rather than just '2nd' or '7th'. (It *is* acceptable to say just 'octave' rather than 'perfect octave', however.) Sometimes, as here, you gain one mark for the type of interval ('major', 'minor' etc.), another for the size ('2nd', '3rd' etc.).

(d) Name the key and cadence at bars 14 to 15.

Key .... Cadence .... *(2)*

(e) Name the key and chord at bar 16 (beat 3).

Key .... Chord .... *(2)*

(f) Describe the piano bass line in bars 24 to 27 (beat 2).

....

.... *(2)*

(g) An accidental has been missed out in bar 27. Insert it at the appropriate place on the stave below.

(1)

(h) Put a cross in the box next to the year in which this music was composed.

☐ **A** 1777

☐ **B** 1827

☐ **C** 1877

☐ **D** 1927 *(1)*

(Total 16 marks)

2015 Test 5   **CD 2 Track 8, 0:00–0:55**

You will hear an excerpt from the first movement of Sonata for Horn, Trumpet and Trombone by Poulenc. A skeleton score of this excerpt is provided below. Bar numbers in this question refer to the skeleton score.

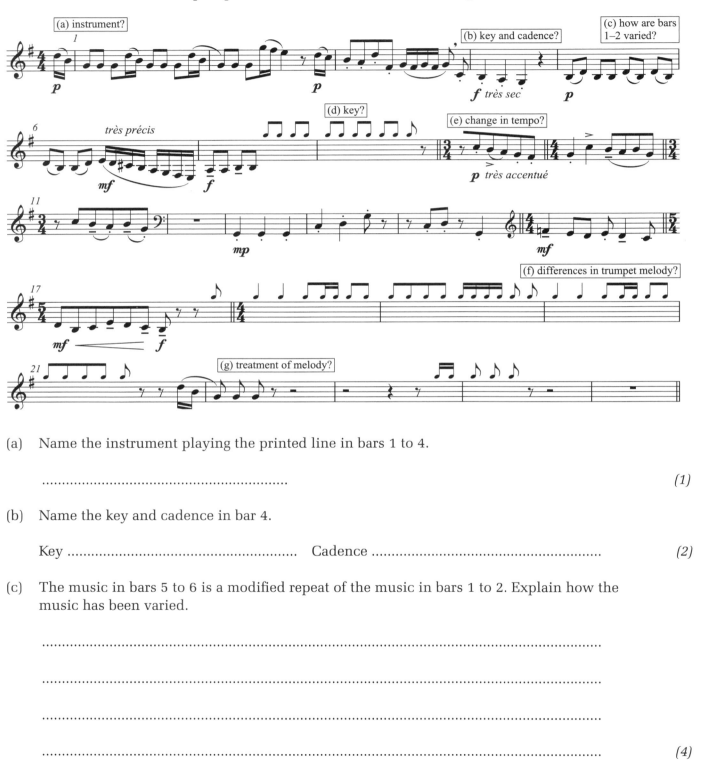

(a)   Name the instrument playing the printed line in bars 1 to 4.

....   *(1)*

(b)   Name the key and cadence in bar 4.

Key ....   Cadence ....   *(2)*

(c)   The music in bars 5 to 6 is a modified repeat of the music in bars 1 to 2. Explain how the music has been varied.

....

....

....

....   *(4)*

Bear in mind that familiar list of musical elements (melody, rhythm, harmony, texture and so on): you're likely to have to address more than one of these to be able to find the four points necessary to score full marks on this question.

(d) Name the key at bar 8.

.... *(1)*

(e) Is the music faster or slower at bar 9?

.... *(1)*

(f) How does the trumpet melody in bars 20 to 21 differ from that in bars 18 to 19?

....

....

.... *(3)*

(g) How does Poulenc treat the melody in bars 22 to 25?

....

.... *(2)*

(h) Put a cross in the box next to the statement that is true.

☐ A The excerpt is part of a binary-form movement

☐ B The excerpt is part of a sonata-form movement

☐ C The excerpt is part of a rondo

☐ D The excerpt is the first part of a ternary-form movement *(1)*

(i) Put a cross in the box next to the statement that is true

☐ A This work is best described as Classical

☐ B This work is best described as modern

☐ C This work is best described as Neoclassical

☐ D This work is best described as Romantic *(1)*

(Total 16 marks)

2015 Test 6   CD 4 Track 14, 0:00–1:10

You will hear an excerpt from 'Tupelo Honey' by Van Morrison. A skeleton score of this excerpt is provided below. Bar numbers in this question refer to the skeleton score.

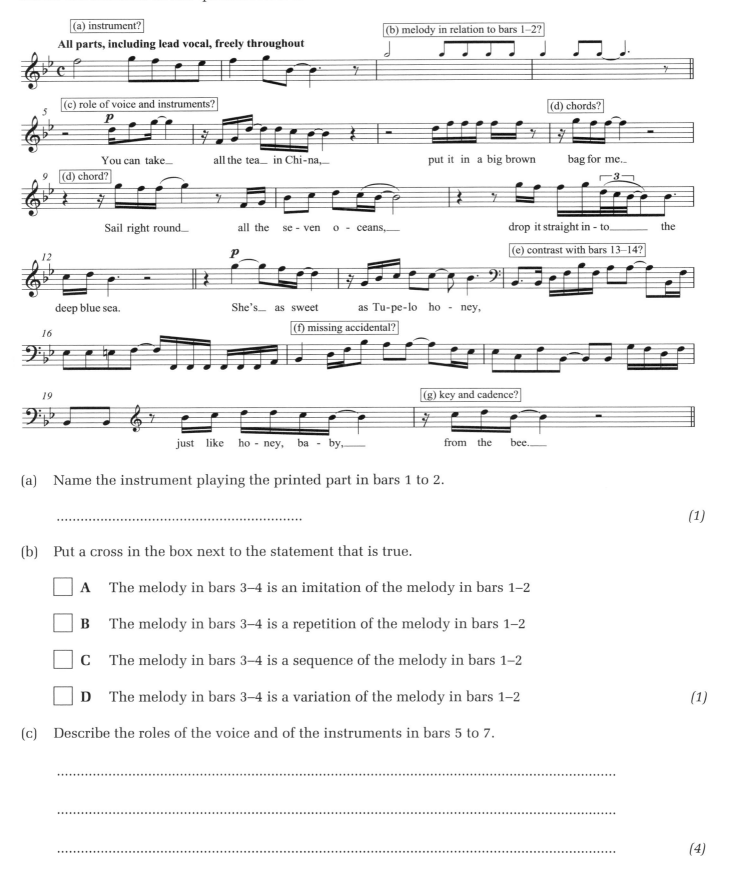

(a)   Name the instrument playing the printed part in bars 1 to 2.

      ....   *(1)*

(b)   Put a cross in the box next to the statement that is true.

      ☐ **A**   The melody in bars 3–4 is an imitation of the melody in bars 1–2

      ☐ **B**   The melody in bars 3–4 is a repetition of the melody in bars 1–2

      ☐ **C**   The melody in bars 3–4 is a sequence of the melody in bars 1–2

      ☐ **D**   The melody in bars 3–4 is a variation of the melody in bars 1–2   *(1)*

(c)   Describe the roles of the voice and of the instruments in bars 5 to 7.

      ....

      ....

      ....   *(4)*

(d) Complete the following table of chords.

Bar 7 (beat 1)	B♭
Bar 7 (beat 3)	Dm/A
Bar 8 (beat 1)	
Bar 8 (beat 3)	
Bar 9 (beat 1)	

(3)

In questions on popular music and jazz, chords are best described using chord symbols (Em, G⁷ etc.), as the table above makes clear. Notice how the given chords for bar 7 set the scene and help you to put bar 8 in its harmonic context.

(e) How does the melody in the lead vocal in bars 15 to 16 differ from the given lead vocal melody in bars 13 to 14?

....

....

.... *(3)*

(f) An accidental has been missed out in bar 17. Insert it at the appropriate point in the stave below:

(1)

(g) Name the key and cadence in bar 20.

Key .... Cadence .... *(2)*

(h) Put a cross in the box next to the statement that is true.

☐ A   The lead vocal melody uses the major scale throughout

☐ B   The lead vocal melody uses the minor scale throughout

☐ C   The lead vocal melody uses the pentatonic scale throughout

☐ D   The lead vocal melody uses the whole-tone scale throughout *(1)*

(Total 16 marks)

2015 Test 7

CD 2 Track 12, 0:00–1:00

You will hear an excerpt from the first movement of Sonata in B flat, K. 333 by Mozart. A skeleton score of this excerpt is provided below. Bar numbers in this question refer to the skeleton score.

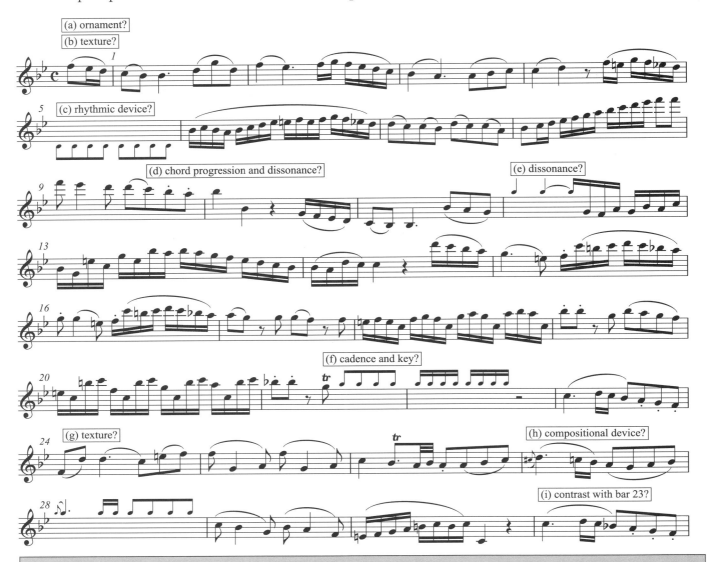

We haven't provided any 'helpful hints' with this test (or in some of the other tests that follow), as you need to get used to managing without them as you prepare for the exam.

(a) An ornament symbol has been omitted from the skeleton score right at the start of the excerpt. Insert it in the stave below:

(1)

(b) Describe the texture of bars 1 to 4, including the number of parts involved.

....

....

(2)

(c)   Name the rhythmic device in the upper part of bar 5. .... (1)

(d)   Comment on the chord progression and dissonance treatment from bar 9 (beat 3) to bar 10 (beat 3).

....

....

.... (4)

(e)   Name the type of dissonance used on the first crotchet beat of bar 12.

.... (1)

(f)   Complete the following sentence.

In bars 21 to 22, there is a(n) .... cadence

in the key of .... (2)

(g)   Which one word best describes the texture in bars 24 to 25?

.... (1)

(h)   Name the compositional device used in bars 27 to 28. .... (1)

(i)   Contrast bar 31 with bar 23. .... (1)

(j)   Put a cross in the box next to the statement that is true.

The overall structure of the piece from which this excerpt is taken is:

☐ **A**   Binary form

☐ **B**   Sonata form

☐ **C**   Ritornello form

☐ **D**   Rondo form   (1)

(k)   Put a cross in the box next to the statement that is true

☐ **A**   This excerpt comes from a Baroque work

☐ **B**   This excerpt comes from a Classical work

☐ **C**   This excerpt comes from an early Romantic work

☐ **D**   This excerpt comes from a late Romantic work   (1)

(Total 16 marks)

2015 Test 8   CD 4 Track 12, 1:54–2:50

You will hear an excerpt from 'Waterloo Sunset' by Ray Davies, as recorded by The Kinks. A skeleton score of this excerpt is provided below. Bar numbers in this question refer to the skeleton score.

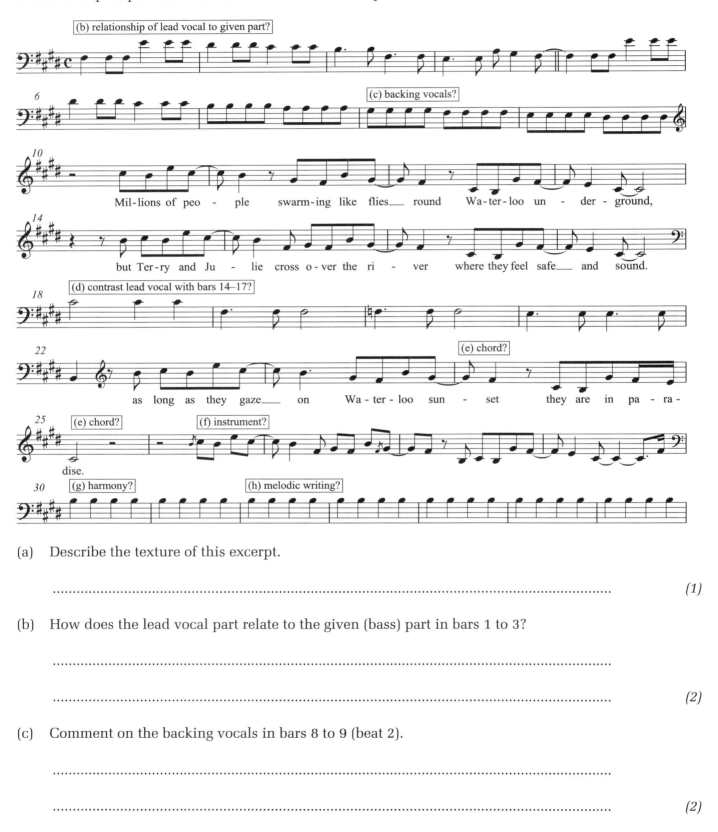

(a)   Describe the texture of this excerpt.

      .... *(1)*

(b)   How does the lead vocal part relate to the given (bass) part in bars 1 to 3?

      ....

      .... *(2)*

(c)   Comment on the backing vocals in bars 8 to 9 (beat 2).

      ....

      .... *(2)*

(d) How does the lead vocal in bars 18 to 21 differ from the lead vocal in bars 14 to 17?

....

.... *(2)*

(e) Complete the following table of chords.

Bar 23	E
Bar 24	
Bar 25	

(2)

(f) Name the instrument playing the given part in bars 26 to 29.

.... *(1)*

(g) Describe the harmony in bars 30 to 36.

....

.... *(2)*

(h) Comment on the melodic writing in bars 32 to 36.

....

....

.... *(3)*

(i) Put a cross in the box next to the statement that is true.

☐ **A** This excerpt opens with the bridge

☐ **B** This excerpt opens with the middle eight

☐ **C** This excerpt opens with the turnaround

☐ **D** This excerpt opens with the verse *(1)*

(Total 16 marks)

2015 Test 9   **CD 1 Track 1, 3:03–3:54**

You will hear an excerpt from the first movement of Brandenburg Concerto No. 4 in G by J. S. Bach. A skeleton score of this excerpt is provided below. Bar numbers in this question refer to the skeleton score.

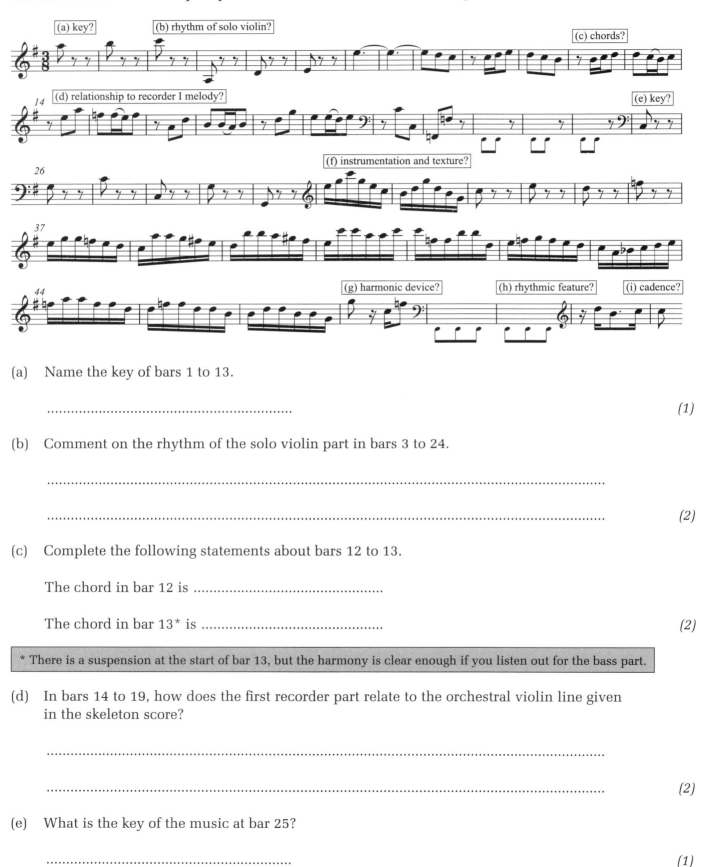

(a) Name the key of bars 1 to 13.

....   *(1)*

(b) Comment on the rhythm of the solo violin part in bars 3 to 24.

....

....   *(2)*

(c) Complete the following statements about bars 12 to 13.

The chord in bar 12 is ....

The chord in bar 13* is ....   *(2)*

> * There is a suspension at the start of bar 13, but the harmony is clear enough if you listen out for the bass part.

(d) In bars 14 to 19, how does the first recorder part relate to the orchestral violin line given in the skeleton score?

....

....   *(2)*

(e) What is the key of the music at bar 25?

....   *(1)*

(f)   Comment on the instrumentation and texture at bars 31 to 36.

....

....

....

....   *(4)*

(g)   Name the harmonic device used in bars 47 to 48.

....   *(1)*

(h)   What is the correct term for the type of of syncopation heard in bars 49 to 50?

....   *(1)*

(i)   Name the cadence at the end of the excerpt.

....   *(1)*

(j)   Put a cross in the box next to the statement that is true.

☐ **A**   This excerpt is the central ritornello

☐ **B**   This excerpt is purely episodic

☐ **C**   This excerpt is a combination of episode and central ritornello

☐ **D**   This excerpt is the opening of the final ritornello   *(1)*

(Total 16 marks)

2015 Test 10   CD 3 Track 10, 0:00–1:06

You will hear an excerpt from 'The Lamb' by John Tavener. A skeleton score of this excerpt is provided below. Bar numbers in this question refer to the skeleton score.

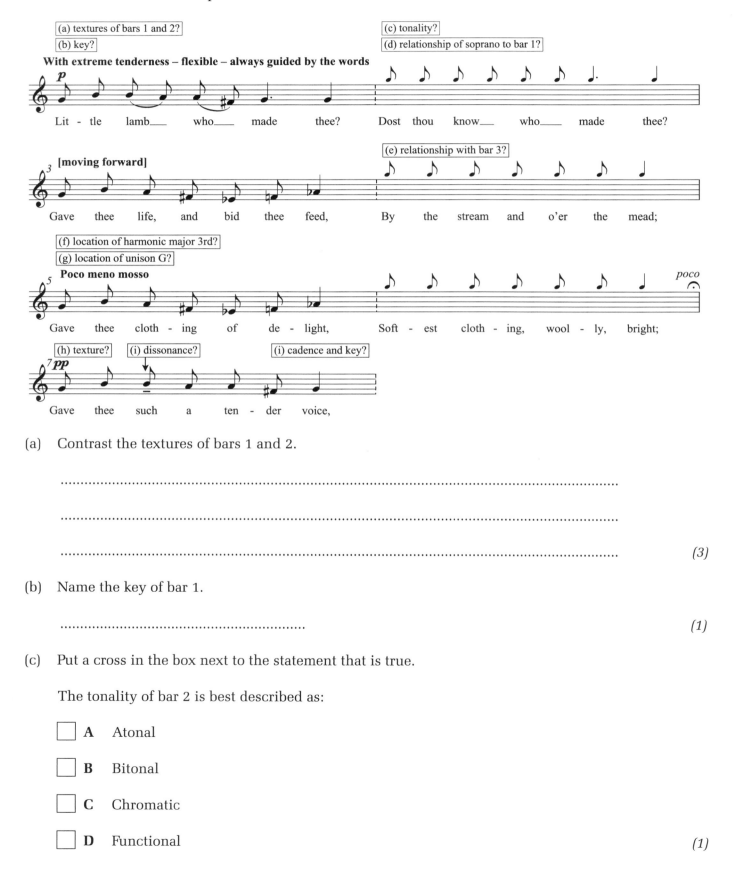

(a) Contrast the textures of bars 1 and 2.

....

....

....   *(3)*

(b) Name the key of bar 1.

....   *(1)*

(c) Put a cross in the box next to the statement that is true.

The tonality of bar 2 is best described as:

☐ **A**   Atonal

☐ **B**   Bitonal

☐ **C**   Chromatic

☐ **D**   Functional   *(1)*

(d) How does the soprano part in bar 2 relate to the soprano part in bar 1?

.... (1)

(e) How does the given part in bar 4 relate to bar 3?

.... (1)

(f) A harmonic* major 3rd can be heard in bar 5. Identify its location by saying on which quaver of the bar it comes (e.g. first, second, third, etc.).

.... (1)

* Harmonic intervals occur when the notes sound together, rather than one after the other.

(g) In bars 5 to 6, there is a unison G on the word 'Gave'. On what other word do you hear the same interval?

.... (1)

(h) Describe the texture of bar 7.

....

.... (2)

(i) Complete the following statements.

The dissonance in the soprano on the third quaver of bar 7 is a(n) ....

The final cadence is ....

The final key is.. (4)

(j) Put a cross in the box next to the statement that is true.

☐ A   The excerpt is taken from an anthem

☐ B   The excerpt is taken from a chorale

☐ C   The excerpt is taken from a madrigal

☐ D   The excerpt is taken from a motet (1)

(Total 16 marks)

You will hear an excerpt from the first movement of String Quartet No. 8, Op. 110 by Shostakovich. A skeleton score of this excerpt is provided below. Bar numbers in this question refer to the skeleton score.

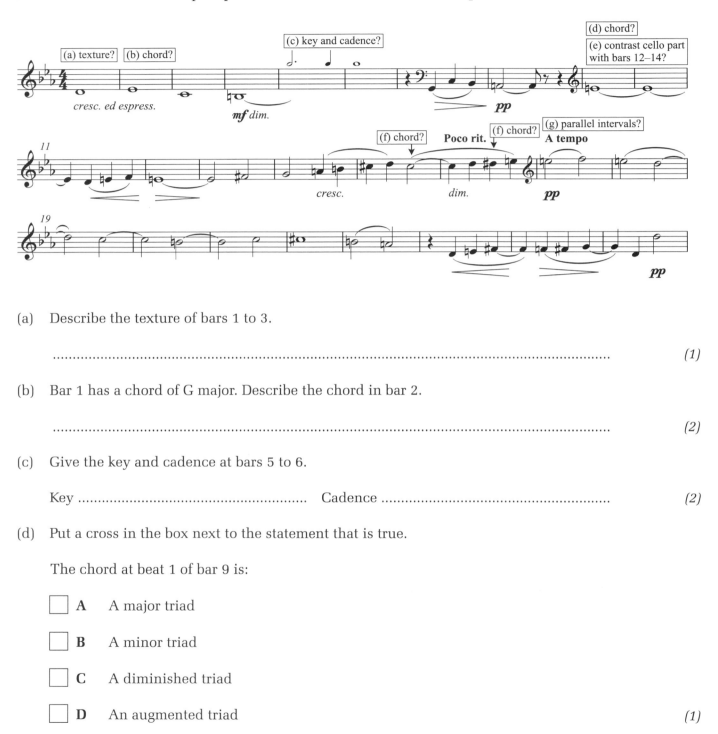

(a)   Describe the texture of bars 1 to 3.

....   *(1)*

(b)   Bar 1 has a chord of G major. Describe the chord in bar 2.

....   *(2)*

(c)   Give the key and cadence at bars 5 to 6.

Key ....   Cadence ....   *(2)*

(d)   Put a cross in the box next to the statement that is true.

The chord at beat 1 of bar 9 is:

☐   **A**   A major triad

☐   **B**   A minor triad

☐   **C**   A diminished triad

☐   **D**   An augmented triad   *(1)*

(e) Compare and contrast the cello part of bars 9 to 11 with the cello part of bars 12 to 14.

....

....

....

....   *(4)*

(f) Complete the statements by adding one of the following letters or words in each of the three spaces:

      C   **F♯**   **major**   **minor**

The chord at bar 15 (beat 3) is F♯ ....

The chord at bar 16 (beat 4) is ....   *(3)*

(g) Bars 17 to 26 include various parallel intervals. Which **two** of the following do we hear? Put crosses in the boxes next to the two statement that are true:

   ☐ **A**   Parallel 3rds between violin I and violin II

   ☐ **B**   Parallel 4ths between violin I and violin II

   ☐ **C**   Parallel 5ths between violin I and violin II

   ☐ **D**   Parallel 5ths between viola and cello

   ☐ **E**   Parallel 6ths between violin I and viola   *(2)*

(h) Put a cross in the box next to the statement that is true.

   ☐ **A**   This excerpt is the opening of the first movement

   ☐ **B**   This excerpt is the recapitulation of the start of the first movement

   ☐ **C**   This excerpt is followed by a partial reprise of the first section of the movement

   ☐ **D**   This excerpt leads directly into the second movement   *(1)*

(Total 16 marks)

2015 Test 12   **CD 3 Track 13, 1:37–2:42**

You will hear an excerpt from 'Ohimè, se tanto amate' by Monteverdi. A skeleton score of this excerpt is provided below. Bar numbers in this question refer to the skeleton score.

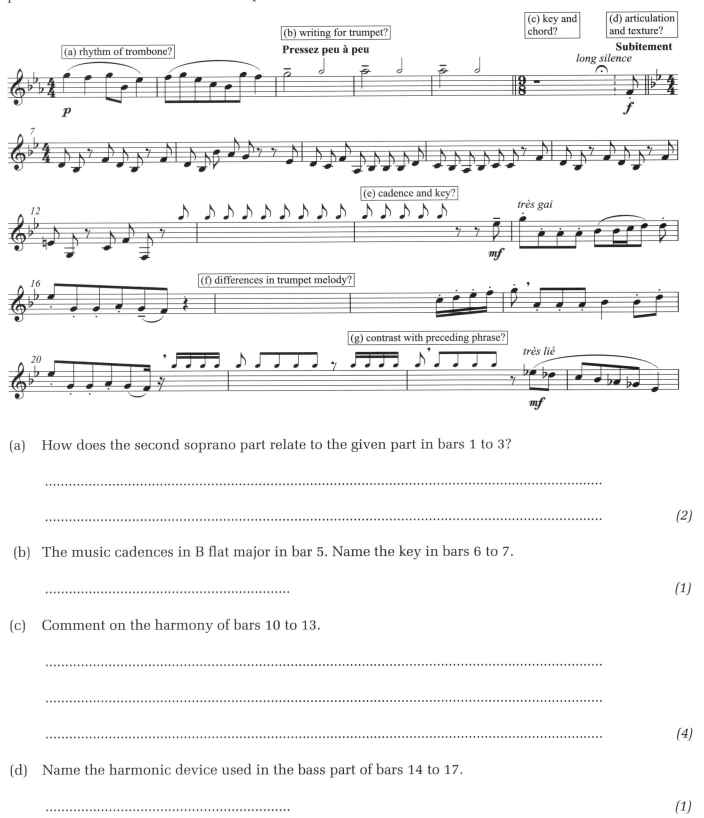

(a) How does the second soprano part relate to the given part in bars 1 to 3?

....

.... *(2)*

(b) The music cadences in B flat major in bar 5. Name the key in bars 6 to 7.

.... *(1)*

(c) Comment on the harmony of bars 10 to 13.

....

....

.... *(4)*

(d) Name the harmonic device used in the bass part of bars 14 to 17.

.... *(1)*

(e) Describe the texture at bar 18 (beat 2) to bar 19 (beat 2).

....

.... *(2)*

(f) How many voice parts do you hear in bars 19 (beat 4) to 23 (beat 3)?

.... *(1)*

(g) Comment on the cadence at bars 28 (beat 4) to 29.

....

.... *(2)*

(h) Mention some devices, not previously referred to, which help to emphasise the meaning of the text.

....

.... *(2)*

(i) Put a cross in the box next to the statement that is true.

This excerpt comes from a work which is an example of:

☐ **A** Early Renaissance style

☐ **B** Prima prattica

☐ **C** Seconda prattica

☐ **D** Late Baroque style *(1)*

(Total 16 marks)

You will hear an excerpt from the first movement of the Sonata for Horn, Trumpet and Trombone by Poulenc. A skeleton score of this excerpt is provided below. Bar numbers in this question refer to the skeleton score.

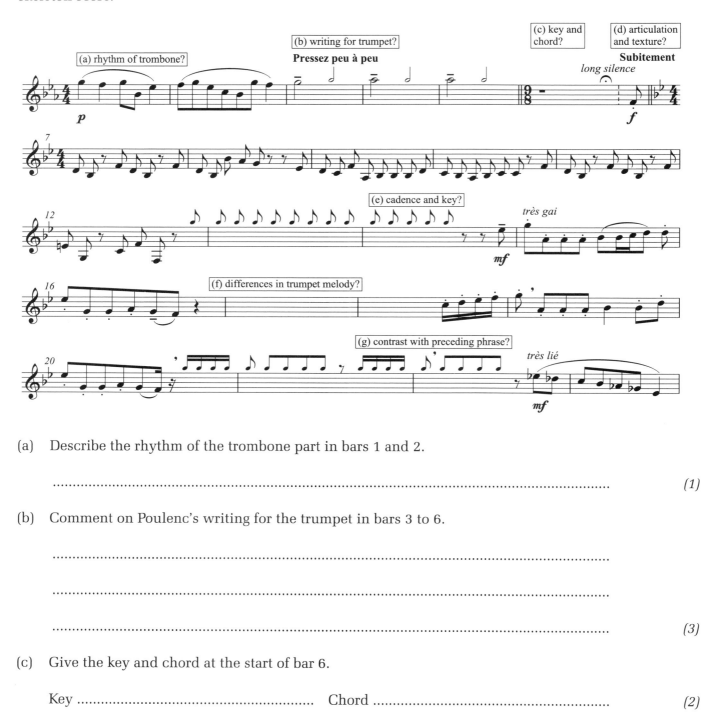

(a)   Describe the rhythm of the trombone part in bars 1 and 2.

.... *(1)*

(b)   Comment on Poulenc's writing for the trumpet in bars 3 to 6.

....

....

.... *(3)*

(c)   Give the key and chord at the start of bar 6.

Key ....   Chord .... *(2)*

(d) Comment on the articulation and texture of bars 6 (last quaver) to 12.

....

....

.... *(3)*

(e) Complete the following sentence.

At bar 14 there is a(n) .... cadence

in the key of .... *(2)*

(f) How does the trumpet melody of bars 16 (last quaver) to bar 18 differ from the trumpet melody of bars 14 (last quaver) to 16?

....

.... *(2)*

(g) How do bars 21 (beat 4) to 22 (beat 3) differ from bars 20 (beat 4) to 21 (beat 3)?

....

.... *(2)*

(h) Put a cross in the box next to the statement that is true.

☐ **A** This excerpt comes from the development section

☐ **B** This excerpt comes from the end of the central section of the movement

☐ **C** This excerpt leads into the coda

☐ **D** This excerpt is a trio section *(1)*

(Total 16 marks)

2015 Test 14  **CD 4 Track 14, 2:06–2:58**

You will hear an excerpt from 'Tupelo Honey' by Van Morrison. A skeleton score of this excerpt is provided below. Bar numbers in this question refer to the skeleton score.

(a) Name the instrument playing the given part in bars 1 to 4.

.... *(1)*

(b) Describe the texture in bars 1 to 8*.

....

....

....

.... *(4)*

* Notice there are four marks for this question. Try to give a general term for the way the parts are combined, and then comment on the role played by individual instruments.

(c) Three pitches have been omitted from the given melody line in bar 6. Insert them on the stave below, using the rhythm given:

(3)

(d)   In bar 9, the acoustic guitar part is given. Comment on the rhythm and melody of the **electric** guitar in this bar.

....

.... *(2)*

(e)   Comment on the rhythm of the electric and acoustic guitar parts in bars 13 to 14.

....

.... *(2)*

(f)   Complete the following table of chords:

Bar 15 (beat 1)	B♭
Bar 15 (beat 3)	
Bar 16 (beat 1)	
Bar 16 (beat 3)	

(g)   Put a cross in the box next to the statement that is true.

☐ **A**   This excerpt is the bridge

☐ **B**   This excerpt is the instrumental

☐ **C**   This excerpt is the middle eight

☐ **D**   This excerpt is the chorus *(1)*

(Total 16 marks)

2015 Test 15   **CD 2 Track 12, 4:02–5:09**

You will hear an excerpt from the first movement of Sonata in B flat, K. 333 by Mozart. A skeleton score of this excerpt is provided below. Bar numbers in this question refer to the skeleton score.

(a)   Compare the melody from bar 2 (beat 4) to bar 4 (beat 2) with that of the preceding two bars.

....   *(1)*

(b) Complete the following sentences.

The chord at bar 6 is a .... chord which

leads in bar 7 to an F major tonic chord in .... inversion.

The chord on the last quaver of bar 7 is chord .... and

it is part of a(n) .... cadence.   *(4)*

(c) Name the key into which the music suddenly moves at bar 8.

....   *(1)*

(d) Describe the texture used in bars 8 to 17.

....   *(2)*

(e) Name the rhythmic device used in the melody at bars 10 to 11.

....   *(1)*

(f) Name the key and cadence at bars 17 (beat 4) to 18 (beat 1).

Key ....

Cadence ....   *(2)*

(g) In bars 24 to 30, do the chords change more or less frequently than previously?

....   *(1)*

(h) Complete the following statements.

In bar 31, the music is in the key of ....

The dissonance on beat 1 of bar 32 is a(n)..

The dissonance on beat 1 of bar 34 is a(n) ....   *(3)*

(i) Put a cross in the box next to the statement that is true.

☐ **A** This excerpt forms the exposition section

☐ **B** This excerpt is the bridge passage

☐ **C** This excerpt is the entire development and opening bars of the recapitulation

☐ **D** This excerpt is the recapitulation   *(1)*

(Total 16 marks)

CD 4 Track 21, 0:00–0:50

You will hear an excerpt from 'Se quema la chumbambá' as recorded by Familia Valera Miranda. A skeleton score of this excerpt is provided below. Bar numbers in this question refer to the skeleton score.

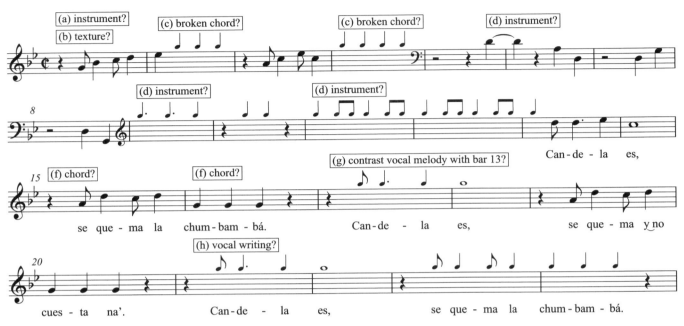

(a) Name the instrument playing the given part in bars 1 to 4.

.... *(1)*

(b) Describe the texture in bars 1 to 2.

.... *(1)*

(c) Identify the broken chords in bars 2 and 4.

Bar 2 ....

Bar 4 .... *(2)*

(d) Name the instruments playing the given parts at the following points:

Bars 5 to 8 ....

Bars 9 to 10 ....

Bars 11 to 12 .... *(3)*

(e) What other percussion instrument do you hear?

.... *(1)*

(f) Name the chords in bars 15 and 16.

Bar 15 ....

Bar 16 ....   *(2)*

(g) How does the vocal melody in bar 17 differ from that in bar 13?

....

....   *(2)*

(h) Describe the vocal writing in bars 21 to 24.

....

....   *(2)*

(i) Put a cross in the box next to the statement that is true.

☐ A   This excerpt is from a calypso

☐ B   This excerpt is from a rumba

☐ C   This excerpt is from a salsa

☐ D   This excerpt is from a son   *(1)*

(j) Put a cross in the box next to the statement that is true

☐ A   This excerpt shows the influence of Mexican music

☐ B   This excerpt shows the influence of Trinidadian music

☐ C   This excerpt shows the influence of African and Spanish music

☐ D   This excerpt shows the influence of Peruvian music   *(1)*

(Total 16 marks)

Section B (Investigating Musical Styles)

Section B of Unit 3 is already well covered in several other Rhinegold Education books, in particular the *Edexcel AS Music Revision Guide, 3rd edition*. Here we shall simply outline what is required for Section B and provide some basic advice on how to tackle the questions.

Do I answer Question 3 (a) or Question 3 (b)?

For Section B you specialise in one area of study (either Instrumental Music or Vocal Music). If you choose Instrumental Music, you answer Question 3 (a) in the exam; if you choose Vocal Music, you answer Question 3 (b). Each question is in two parts, (i) and (ii): you answer both parts from your chosen question.

Part (i) is worth 10 marks, and will relate to just one of the set works. Part (ii) is worth 18 marks, and involves comparing and contrasting two different set works.

You can answer in full sentences, in note form or by using bullet points, provided your work is clear, accurate, neat and well-organised.

During the two-hour exam, it's probably sensible to spend *at least* 45 minutes on Section B (given that Section A, which is timed for you, will take 25 minutes or so, and that there is also Section C, with two questions to do). You may be wise to spend not less than 15 minutes on Part (i), and not less than 30 minutes on Part (ii), since Part (ii) carries almost twice as many marks as Part (i).

Part (i): the 10-mark question

The 10-mark question requires you to write about one of the set works in terms of its style. For example, you'll need to explain what makes the work Renaissance, Baroque, Classical, and so on. A typical question might look like this:

'Describe the stylistic features of 'Der Doppelgänger' by Schubert which show that this music was composed in the Romantic era.'

When your exam paper is marked, the examiner will count up the number of relevant points that you have made. Among these points you can gain credit for up to three examples or bits of extra detail (which might occasionally include, if relevant, short quotations from the score).

The total number of points, including examples, will often translate into the same number of marks. However, the examiner will rate your answer not just on its number of relevant points, but also in terms of its overall quality, using a marking grid which contains words such as 'Outstanding', 'Excellent', 'Confident' and 'Competent'. Seven points would normally take you into the 'Competent' category, which has 7 marks. But a seven-point answer *could* be rated 'Confident' (8 marks) – perhaps if there were some really good examples, or some points were made very well. Don't be afraid, therefore, to give *more* than three examples if you are able.

Your mark could also go up or down a little based on your quality of written communication (or QWC). So always try to:

➤ Write clearly
➤ Only include information that is relevant
➤ Organise the points you make in a logical order
➤ Spell words correctly (especially remember 'rhythm' and 'bass'). Abbreviations used in texting, such as 'c u l8r', are not acceptable
➤ Punctuate correctly
➤ Use correct grammar.

These things apply whether you write in continuous prose, in note form, or with bullet points.

Part (ii): the 18-mark question

The 18-mark question requires you to compare and contrast two set works in terms of two musical features (for example, harmony and rhythm). The following are the musical features you may have to write about:

➤ Resources
➤ Form
➤ Texture
➤ Tonality
➤ Harmony
➤ Melody
➤ Rhythm and metre.

A typical question might be:

'Compare and contrast the form and tonality of Pavane 'The image of melancholy' and Galliard 'Ecce quam bonum' by Holborne with Symphony No. 26, first movement by Haydn.'

As in Part (i), the examiner will count up the number of relevant points that you make. But among these points may be up to six examples. The total number of points, including examples, will normally translate into the same number of marks (for example, 12 points, including three examples, will normally give you 12 marks out of the possible maximum of 18).

However, the examiner will also assess your answer in terms of its overall impression, using a mark scheme which contains words such as 'Outstanding', 'Excellent', 'Confident' and 'Competent', and may adjust the final mark as a result.

Using examples

The more you listen to the set works, the more detail you'll remember and the easier it will be to give examples about particular features in your answers. It's rather like doing a particular journey regularly: you soon begin to recall names of roads and other landmarks, sharp bends, steep hills and so on.

Try this short exercise:

> ➢ Listen several times (without the score) to the beginning of the first movement from Haydn's Symphony No. 26 (from the Edexcel Anthology CD 1, track 2 as far as about 0 minutes, 30 seconds).

Now read the following:

> ➢ The music begins in a minor key, with strings and wind. It's very agitated, with the two main melodic lines cutting across one another all the time in syncopation.

> ➢ Then there's a 'sighing' passage for strings and horns, again minor, with the same two chords (I and Vb) over and over, always separated by rests, followed by a short return to the opening syncopated rhythms.

> ➢ A brighter major-key section follows with a tune that begins with repeated notes in the oboe and second violins.

Listen to the music again. Could you follow the journey?

How should you refer to examples in the exam, since you won't have a copy of the Anthology with you? Think again of a familiar journey. You might, for example, identify something as happening 'between x and y' or 'near that steep hill leading down into z'. With music, we might rather similarly refer to 'the opening bars' or 'the middle section'. The better you know the musical journey, the easier it is to give the examiner clear directions: 'at the start of the development section' is jargon that he or she will understand and appreciate. If you *can* remember bar numbers, that's fine – but quoting bar numbers from memory is sometimes a bit like having map references or postcodes in your head when you're out for a walk.

Section C (Understanding Chords and Lines)

Section C of the Unit 3 exam has two questions: Question 4 (harmonic analysis) and Question 5 (completing an SATB texture). You may need to allow as much as 45 minutes for Section C, perhaps with about 15–18 minutes on Question 4 and about 27–30 minutes on Question 5. But lots of practice may mean that you can get through Section C more quickly than this, thus leaving yourself with more time for Section B and/ or for checking answers at the end of the exam.

Question 4: Analysis of Harmony

For Question 4 you must be prepared to identify chords, key(s) and modulations, cadences, and non-chord (also called 'non-harmonic') notes. Non-chord or non-harmonic notes are those which, like passing notes, don't belong to the chord sounding at the time. For example:

Because only 8 marks are awarded for Question 4, you may not be tested on everything listed above, but it is virtually certain that you will have to identify several chords in terms of Roman numerals. There are no choices with Question 4: you must answer all (probably about four or five) parts.

The *AS Music Harmony Workbook* by Hugh Benham (Rhinegold Education, 2008) provides in-depth help with harmonic analysis. It should constantly be at hand: the book you are reading at this moment provides exercises, but does not tell you about how to analyse chords, changes of key and so on.

A complete (*not* skeleton) score for the music you have to analyse will be provided. It will be on three staves, the highest for voice (with words), the others for piano.

No recording of the music for Question 4 will be provided in the exam. You must therefore do your analysis from the score. This is an important skill needed for more advanced analysis, but if you can hear the music in your head at least some of the time then this will make the exercise more musical and less theoretical.

Here are some tips for answering the analysis questions:

1. **Read each part of the question thoroughly**. Do exactly what it asks.
2. **Carefully identify the key.** Identifying the key is an important first step to labelling the chords used in the music. To help you, one or two of the chords might already be identified (with Roman numerals), but you should not assume that this will always be the case. Remember that exercises for Question 4 may be in major or minor keys, and may have key signatures with up to four sharps or flats.
3. **Take note of any accidentals**. They may indicate key change(s) (although an accidental might also just be chromatic).
4. **Get lots of practice** with playing, reading, listening to and looking at chords, experimenting with non-chord notes and so on.

There are nine tests below to help you prepare for Question 4. These are in different major and minor keys with signatures of four or fewer sharps or flats (to help prepare you for the range of keys from which the examiners can choose when setting analysis questions).

At the ends of Tests 1–3 we have added a few additional questions that can be used for extra practice. There are no marks for these additional questions, but answers are still given in the 'Answers and how to mark them' section on pages 95–108. They can be used as a template for making up your own additional questions for the other tests.

Some tests begin with a *Note* which points out special features or provides hints and tips. Make sure you read any such notes before you start a test.

Blank page

Test 1

Note: To provide a fairly simple start, the music of Test 1 is all in the same key (and is entirely diatonic) until the last couple of bars. Generally, the right hand of the piano part doubles the vocal melody, so if you don't find it easy reading music on three staves, it's usually enough in Test 1 to concentrate on the two staves of the piano part. Incidentally, don't be put off when you see Italian words under the singer's part: you can answer every question without knowing what the text means. Nevertheless, for information, we have provided a translation for each test where the words are not in English.

Study the printed music below and answer all of the questions that follow.

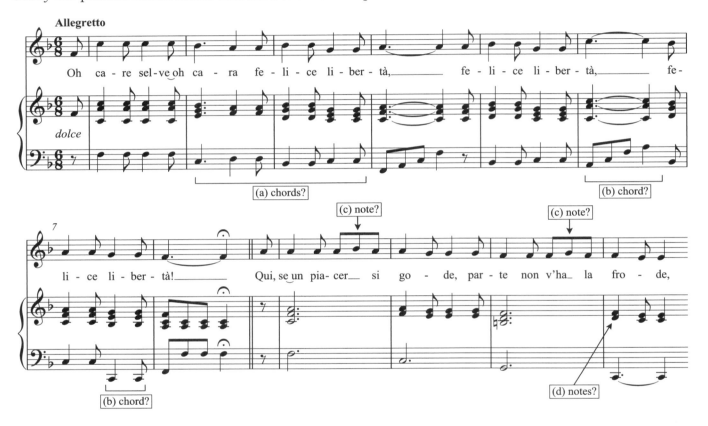

Translation: O dear woods, O dear happy freedom! Here pleasure is enjoyed, and deceit has no place.

(a) Complete the table below to give a harmonic analysis of bars 1 to 4. Precisely indicate, using Roman numerals, the chords that are used.

> The Roman numerals used in harmonic analysis are I, II, III, IV, V, VI and VII (i.e. numbers 1–7). Remember though that in harmonic analysis the full Roman-numeral description of a chord may include additional symbols – for example the b in Ib, or the ⁷ in V⁷.

Bar 1	I
Bar 2 (1st dotted crotchet beat)	
Bar 2 (2nd dotted crotchet beat)	
Bar 3 (1st dotted crotchet beat)	
Bar 3 (2nd dotted crotchet beat)	
Bar 4	I

(4)

(b)   Identify, using Roman numerals, the chords used in:

Bar 6 (all of it, except the final quaver) ....

Look at *all* the notes involved, not just those heard at the beginning of the bar.

Bar 7 (2nd dotted crotchet beat) ....   *(2)*

(c)   Complete the sentence below by putting a cross in the box next to the correct answer.

The B♭ in bar 9 and the G in bar 11 (both in the vocal part) are best described as:

☐ **A**   Appoggiaturas

☐ **B**   Auxiliary notes

☐ **C**   Passing notes

☐ **D**   Suspensions   *(1)*

(d)   Complete the sentence below by putting a cross in the box next to the correct answer.

The D and F in bar 12 (piano, right hand) are best described as:

☐ **A**   Appoggiaturas

☐ **B**   Auxiliary notes

☐ **C**   Passing notes

☐ **D**   Suspensions   *(1)*

(Total 8 marks)

Additional practice questions

(i) Label with Roman numerals any chords in bars 1–10 not already identified. (ii) Into what key does the music go in the last two bars? (iii) What are the two chords used in these bars? (Remember to give Roman numerals in the key that you have just identified for question (ii).) (iv) Identify the types of cadences used in bars 3 to 4 and 7 to 8.

Test 2

Note: In Test 2, the right hand part of the piano duplicates or shadows the vocal part much of the time. But the vocal part is occasionally independent, usually where it has an important non-harmonic note. While you could identify all the chords in question (a) from the piano part alone, you will need to consider the whole texture when answering the other questions. Two more things to note:

➢ The start of a bar or beat may not include all the notes of the chord (as in bar 6 of Test 1).

➢ In piano writing the bass often rests while other notes from the chord are sounded, but is still considered part of the harmony (perhaps being prolonged by the sustaining pedal). Thus we count the whole of bar 1 of Test 2 as chord I: we don't say that the chord changes to Ib at quaver 3.

Study the printed music below and answer all of the questions that follow.

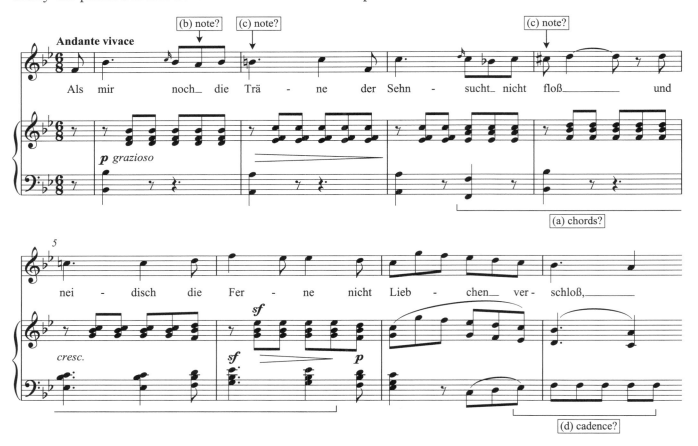

Translation: When tears of longing no longer flowed, and distance no longer jealously imprisoned my beloved...

(a) Complete the table below to give a harmonic analysis of bars 1 to 6. Precisely indicate, using Roman numerals, the chords that are used.

Bar 1	I
Bars 2 to 3 (3rd quaver)	V⁷b
Bar 3 (quavers 4 to 6)	
Bar 4	
Bar 5 (quavers 1 to 5)	
Bar 5 (last quaver)	
Bar 6 (quavers 1 to 5)	

(5)

(b) What type of non-harmonic note is the A in bar 1 of the vocal part?

.... *(1)*

> Questions on non-harmonic (non-chord) notes could be open-ended like this or multiple-choice like the next question. As with any non-harmonic note, consider how the A in bar 1 is approached and quitted. (Clue: it sits between two harmony notes of the same pitch.)

(c) Complete the sentence below by putting a cross in the box next to the correct answer.

The B♮ in bar 2 and the C♯ in bar 4 (both in the vocal part) are best described as:

☐ **A** Anticipations

☐ **B** Appoggiaturas

☐ **C** Auxiliary notes

☐ **D** Suspensions *(1)*

(d) What type of cadence is used at the end of the passage, from bar 7 (last quaver) to bar 8?

.... *(1)*

(Total 8 marks)

> A question on *type* of cadence expects the answer 'perfect', 'imperfect', 'plagal', or 'interrupted' – not Roman numerals (e.g. V–I or IIb–V). In simple styles of music perfect cadences (especially) and imperfect are generally by far the most common.

Additional practice questions

(i) Label with Roman numerals any chords not already identified. (ii) Locate and identify any non-harmonic notes not already identified (don't forget the F at the start of bar 6). (iii) Identify the cadence in bars 3 to 4.

Test 3

Note: Analysis tests can be in minor as well as major keys. Here is your first minor one. Note that in this test, you are asked to identify chords towards the end of the piece *after* the music has modulated (but the new key is given for you in the question).

Study the printed music below and answer all of the questions that follow.

(a)   Complete the following sentence.

At bar 1 beat 3 to bar 2 beat 2 there is a(n) .... cadence

in the key of ....   *(2)*

(b)   Name the cadence in bar 4.

....   *(1)*

(c)   What type of chord is used at bar 5 beat 3?

....   *(1)*

> Here you are asked for the *type* of chord, not for a Roman numeral.

(d)   In bars 10 to 14 the key is G major. Precisely indicate, using Roman numerals, the chords
      that are used.

Bar 11 beats 1 and 2	
Bar 11 beat 3	
Bar 12 beat 1	
Bar 13 beat 1	

(4)

> Note carefully what the question above requires. There is a gap – you are *not* asked for Roman numerals for bar 12, beats
> 2–3. You will need to look at the whole texture to be sure of the chords asked for in this question, because the vocal part
> is more independent of the piano part than in Tests 1 and 2. Also, don't forget that the dotted minim C that begins at bar
> 11 beat 1 continues through beat 3 and forms part of the chord at that point.

(Total 8 marks)

Additional practice questions

(i) Label with Roman numerals any chords not already identified. There are one or two quite tricky corners!
Remember that you must know the key before you can apply Roman numerals correctly. (ii) Locate and
identify non-harmonic notes in the vocal part (e.g. the A in bar 3). (iii) Identify the key and the cadence in
bars 5 to 6, 13 to 14 and 15 to 16. (iv) What harmonic device is used in bar 16?

Test 4

Study the printed music below and answer all of the questions that follow.

(a)   Complete the table below to give a harmonic analysis of bars 2 to 3. Precisely indicate, using Roman numerals, the chords that are used.

Bar 2 beats 3 to 4	
Bar 3 beats 1 to 2	
Bar 3 beat 3	
Bar 3 beat 4	I

(3)

(b)   In what key is the cadence in bar 5?

....   *(1)*

(c)   Complete the sentence below by putting a cross in the box next to the correct answer.

In bar 6 of the vocal part, the quavers G and D are:

☐ **A**   Anticipations

☐ **B**   Appoggiaturas

☐ **C**   Auxiliary notes

☐ **D**   Échappées   *(1)*

(d)   In bar 8, which note in the left hand of the piano part is a diatonic passing note?

....   *(1)*

(e)   In bar 9, what kind of non-harmonic note is the minim B in the right hand of the piano part?

....   *(1)*

(f)   What type of chord is heard at bar 12 beat 4?

....   *(1)*

(Total 8 marks)

Test 5

Study the printed music below and answer all of the questions that follow.

(a) Complete the table below to give a harmonic analysis of bars 6 to 8. Precisely indicate, using Roman numerals, the chords that are used.

Bar 6 beat 1	V
Bar 6 beat 2	I
Bar 6 beat 3	
Bar 7 beat 1	
Bar 7 beat 2	
Bar 7 beat 3	I
Bar 8 beat 1	

(4)

(b) Identify the cadence in bars 3 to 4.

....   *(1)*

(c) Identify the type of chord used at bar 9 beat 3 and again at bar 11 beat 3.

....   *(1)*

(d) Identify the key of bar 10.

....   *(1)*

(e) Complete the sentence below by putting a cross in the box next to the correct answer.

The A♯ in the piano part (left hand) of bar 15 is best described as a chromatic:

☐ **A**   Appoggiatura

☐ **B**   Auxiliary note

☐ **C**   Échappée

☐ **D**   Passing note   *(1)*

(Total 8 marks)

Test 6

Note: This test is intended to give you further practice with minor keys, and a chance to work with music with the maximum number of flats permitted for this type of question.

Study the printed music below and answer all of the questions that follow.

Translation: Jesus bowed his head and died! See the other Adam sleep, who woos our souls.

(a) Complete the table below to give a harmonic analysis of bars 1 to 7. Precisely indicate, using Roman numerals, the chords that are used. All of the chords are in the tonic key.

Bar 1	I
Bar 2	
Bar 3	
Bar 7 (beats 1 and 2)	
Bar 7 (beat 3)	

(4)

(b) Name the harmonic device used in bar 8.

....

(1)

(c) Look at bars 9 to 14. Identify, in the vocal part, one example of each of the following types of non-harmonic note, by supplying the letter name of the note and its bar number.

Anticipation   letter name: ....   bar number: ....

Échappée   letter name: ....   bar number: ....   *(2)*

(d) Identify the key in bars 16 to 18.

....

(1)

(Total 8 marks)

Test 7

Note: Test 7 has the maximum number of sharps permitted for the Section C analysis question.

Study the printed music below and answer all of the questions that follow.

(a)   Complete the table below to give a harmonic analysis of bars 3 to 4. Precisely indicate, using Roman numerals, the chords that are used.

Bar 3 beat 2	I
Bar 3 beat 3	
Bar 3 beat 4	
Bar 4 beats 1 and 2	

(3)

(b)   Identify the key at:

Bars 8 to 9 ....

Bars 10 to 14 ....

(2)

(c)   What type of non-harmonic note is heard in the vocal part at bar 11 beat 1?

....

(1)

(d)   Complete the sentence below by putting a cross in the box next to the correct answer.

The B at bar 12 beat 4 (piano, right-hand part) and the B at bar 13 beat 4 are best described as:

☐   **A**   Appoggiaturas

☐   **B**   Auxiliary notes

☐   **C**   Échappées

☐   **D**   Suspensions

(1)

Note that both hands of the piano part are written in the bass clef here.

(e)   What type of cadence is used both in bars 1 to 2 and in bars 13 to 14?

....

(1)

(Total 8 marks)

Test 8

Study the printed music below and answer all of the questions that follow.

(a) Complete the table below to give a harmonic analysis of bars 1 to 9. Precisely indicate, using Roman numerals, the chords that are used. All of the chords are in the tonic key.

Note that the piano part begins with the treble clef in both hands.

Bar 1 beats 1 and 3	Ib
Bar 1 beat 4	
Bar 8 beats 1 and 2	
Bar 8 beats 3 and 4	
Bar 9 beats 1 and 2	

(4)

(b) Identify the type of non-harmonic note heard at bar 3 beat 3.

....

(1)

(c) Identify the key at:

Bar 11 ....

Bar 12 beat 4 to bar 14 beat 1 ....

(2)

(d) Complete the sentence below by putting a cross in the box next to the correct answer.

Bar 15 includes, on beats 1, 2 and 3:

☐ **A**   A passing note, an échappée and a suspension

☐ **B**   A passing note, an auxiliary note and a suspension

☐ **C**   A passing note, an auxiliary note and an appoggiatura

☐ **D**   A passing note, an anticipation and a suspension

(1)

(Total 8 marks)

Test 9

Study the printed music below and answer all of the questions that follow.

Translation: A boy saw a little rose growing on the heath. It was so young and morning-fresh, he ran quickly to look closely at it. He gazed at it with much joy. Little rose, little rose, little rose red, little rose on the heath.

(a) Complete the table below to give a harmonic analysis of bars 1 to 4. Precisely indicate, using Roman numerals, the chords that are used.

Bar 1	I
Bar 2	II⁷d
Bar 3 beat 1	
Bar 3 beat 2	
Bar 4 beat 1	

(3)

(b) What type of non-harmonic note is the D in bar 6?

.... *(1)*

(c) Look at the piano part of bars 7 to 10. How does the harmony of bars 9 to 10 **differ** from the harmony of bars 7 to 8?

....

.... *(2)*

(d) Name the type of cadence heard in bar 14.

.... *(1)*

(e) Complete the sentence below by putting a cross in the box next to the correct answer.

On the second quaver beat of bar 16, the demisemiquaver B is best described as an:

☐ **A** Anticipation

☐ **B** Appoggiatura

☐ **C** Auxiliary note

☐ **D** Échappée *(1)*

(Total 8 marks)

Question 5: Harmonising a Melody

For Question 5 you must complete a short passage for soprano, alto, tenor and bass voices. The soprano part will be given throughout, together with the beginnings of the three lower voices. It is likely that *five* chords will have to be completed. There may be *three* given chords (enough to help underline the tonality); if there are more, this is additional help: it certainly doesn't make your job harder.

The exercise in your exam will be printed in short score, with two staves, the higher containing soprano and alto parts, the lower (with a bass clef) tenor and bass. The music will be homophonic (mainly chordal, but perhaps with a few passing notes or other non-chord notes). In terms of style, the closest models are simple 18th- and 19th-century hymn tunes, but if you are already preparing for the Chorale Technical Study for Unit 5, you'll find that much of what you learn about Bach's style will also help here in Unit 3.

Question 5 may be in a major or a minor key, with a key signature of up to three sharps or flats; modulation will not be required. The test will end with a cadence. The majority of cadences are perfect and it is quite likely that your exam exercise will require one. But don't be surprised if that isn't the case. An imperfect cadence may be suggested by the last two notes of the given soprano part (particularly if the melody ends with notes 3–2 or 8–7 of the scale of the key you're in). A plagal cadence may also be suggested, but in simple musical styles plagal cadences are not common. It's never necessary to end with a V–VI interrupted cadence – wherever such a cadence might go, a perfect cadence will also fit and is generally easier to handle.

If you're not sure where to start with Question 5, consider following the steps below:

1. **Carefully identify the key**. If there is an accidental in the melody, it will almost certainly belong to a harmonic or melodic minor scale, and therefore confirm that the exercise is in a minor key.

2. **Write out a chord diagram and label the given chords at the start of the test**.

3. **Choose suitable chords for the cadence**.

4. **Add a cadence approach chord**.

5. **Choose chords for the remaining unharmonised notes**. Make sure that the first chord you add carries on effectively from the last given chord.

6. **Add alto and tenor parts**.

7. **Check everything – especially to make sure you've avoided consecutive 5ths and octaves**.

The *AS Music Harmony Workbook* by Hugh Benham (Rhinegold Education, 2008) includes plenty of information on how to harmonise short melodies: points 1–7 above are all dealt with in chapter 7.

During the exam you will have access to a keyboard on which you can try out what you've written. But it's not the intention that you should sit at the keyboard all the time and doodle away until you get something that sounds right! Try to work with chords so much that you find you're beginning to remember what they will sound like when they're written down. Try also to be really familiar with the 'rules' of harmony and part-writing – all of which are shortcuts to understanding what will sound effective and what will not.

When completing the practice exercises that follow, try increasingly to ration your use of a keyboard.

There are 16 tests below. They include at least one example in each key that you might encounter in the exam.

The instructions for each test are the same. In this book, the instructions are printed once only (for Test 1), but apply to all of the tests. Similarly the words '**(Total 12 marks)**' are printed only after Test 1, but also apply to each subsequent test.

Test 1

Complete the music below for SATB voices in short score choosing suitable chords. Some credit will be given for the appropriate use of non-harmonic notes. You may do rough work on manuscript paper, but you must write your answer on the score.

Note: There is no quaver movement in the given material for Test 1, or in the next two tests. You may prefer to keep it simple at this early stage, and avoid quaver movement in what you add. However, feel free to introduce one or two passing notes if you can find suitable opportunities. Remember that an added passing note may cause consecutives where they would not otherwise exist.

(Total 12 marks)

Test 2

Note: more chords are given at the start of this exercise compared to the last one. This is a reminder that, even though you always have to add five chords, the number of chords you start with may vary. The more chords there are, the easier you should find it to identify the key.

Test 3

Note: This is your first exercise in a minor key – there are three accidentals to prove it! The bass F♯ in bar 2 (a leading note) tells you pretty clearly that the next note in the bass should be G (and the chord should be I).

Test 4

Note: This is the first of a small number of tests not in common time (**C** or $\frac{4}{4}$), partly just for variety, and partly to prove that working short exercises in triple time is not necessarily difficult. There is some quaver movement in the given material this time. The alto's quaver F is a clear sign that the first alto note you write should be E. Only one chord is necessary under the quavers A and G (every test will require you to write five chords).

Test 5

Test 6

Note: The large leap in bar 2 is unusual. Be careful not to have an overlap* here, with the alto on beat 2 higher than the soprano E♭ on beat 1. In this test you have a choice of two types of cadence at the end.

* For advice on overlaps see the *AS Music Harmony Workbook* (Rhinegold Eduction, 2008), page 107.

Test 7

Note: The bass G♮ quaver belongs to the descending melodic minor scale, and shows you clearly what the first bass note in bar 2 should be. Both quavers at bar 2 beat 2 are harmony notes (because of the leap to the A): the chord chosen at this point must therefore include both C and A.

Test 8

Note: Here is an example with a minim rather than a crotchet beat. It's probably unlikely that you will encounter such writing in the exam, but it is worth gaining experience in a variety of metres.

Test 9

Test 10

Note: The use of A♯ and A♮ in the same bar may seem surprising, but it is perfectly logical. The A♯ is the 'ordinary' sharpened leading note, while the A♮ is part of a descending melodic-minor pattern. Try substituting A♯ for the A♮, and you'll hear why the latter is essential – it avoids an awkward augmented 2nd melodic interval between A♯ and G♮. The given tenor part is a little dull, with all its Bs. Such dullness is sometimes almost inevitable in simple and short harmony exercises. But here, if you can, avoid having B in the tenor on beat 2 of bar 3. You will probably need two Bs elsewhere in your added tenor part.

Test 11

Note: The minim C in bar 3, part of a hemiola, will sound dull if all the added parts are also minims.

Test 12

Note: It's possible to begin this test in one key and end it in another (E minor to G major – why most definitely not to B minor?). However, exam exercises won't expect you to modulate.

Test 13

Test 14

Test 15

Test 16

How to find and invent more questions for Unit 3

Here are some hints on finding and inventing practice material in addition to the questions provided in this book. Three other sources with ready-made questions that you could use are:

1. **Past examination papers** (available to download from the Edexcel website). For Section C questions, you can use any of the past exam papers from 2009 to 2013. For Sections A and B, you can only use past-paper questions that relate to either the 2014 or 2015 set works. This means the whole of the 2009 paper is fine to use for 2014, and the 2010 paper for 2015 (as they use the same set works), but you may also be able to find relevant questions on other past papers. For example, there is a Section A question in the 2012 paper on Weelkes' *Sing we at pleasure* (also a 2014 set work).

2. **Edexcel's Sample Assessment Materials** (available to download from the Edexcel website). These were designed to help prepare teachers and students for the 2009 exam in particular (the first exam after the specification changed), but as the 2009 set works are being repeated in 2014, they can still be used as a good source of questions.

3. **Other Rhinegold Education publications.** Additional teaching and practice material for Section C is published in the *AS Music Harmony Workbook*. For additional material on Section B, see the *Edexcel AS Music Revision Guide (3rd edition)*, and the *Edexcel AS Music Study Guide (3rd edition)*.

The alternative approach is to write your own questions, and the next couple of pages will give you some advice on how to do this.

Inventing questions for Section A

➢ In the exam, students need to answer one question on each area of study, so it is wise to cover both areas with equal thoroughness.
➢ Take any set work, and choose any passage that lasts for a minute or slightly more.
➢ Decide on a number of things that could reasonably be answered, given what you expect your students to know at the time you invent the test, and the five hearings of the chosen passage that they will get in the exam.
➢ Questions might be asked, for example, about the texture of particular passages, instrumentation, or the character and development of melodic motifs – or about keys, cadences and chords, or structure.
➢ Look at the tests on pages 9–61, and at past exam papers, for further detail. Questions must be designed to require short responses (often one or two lines, but sometimes just single words, or a letter in response to a multiple-choice item).
➢ In the exam there may be ten or more parts to a Section A question, with 16 marks in total. Some questions are worth one mark; most others carry two or three marks.
➢ A skeleton score must be provided to guide students as they go through the excerpt. This usually shows a slightly incomplete version of the main melody part, designed not to give away the answers. For example, if the desired answer to a question on bars 3–4 is 'sequence', the skeleton score must not show the notes E–F–G–A in bar 3 and D–E–F–G in bar 4. Bracketed cues are given to indicate the bars to which particular questions refer. Look at past papers and the tests in this book to see more clearly how skeleton scores are constructed.

Inventing questions for Section B

10-mark questions

➢ Pick any one of the set works.

➢ A 10-mark question must require this work to be related to its historical or cultural context. It may well be similar in format to the following: 'What musical features of *composer A*'s *work B* indicate that it was composed in the *C period*?'

18-mark questions

➢ Pick any *two* set works from *one* of the areas of study.

➢ An 18-mark question must ask for comparison and contrast of two musical features in the two selected works.* It may well be similar in format to the following: 'Compare and contrast *feature A* and *feature B* in *work C* and *work D*.'

> * Page 63 provides a list of the type of musical features that could be asked about.

➢ In the exam, the two works that feature in the 18-mark question will be different from the single work referred to in the 10-mark question.

Inventing questions for Section C

Practice material for analysis questions

➢ To invent a specimen question, find a piece for single voice and keyboard, notated on three staves.

➢ The music is best taken from 18th- or early 19th-century repertoire (Baroque, Classical or early Romantic). Later music usually has chords that the specification does not require students to identify; most earlier music does not use the necessary kind of simple functional harmony.

➢ Take an extract, lasting 10–20 bars or a little more (depending partly on the length of the bars).

➢ Study carefully the layout and type of questions asked in past papers.

➢ Ask for *eight* pieces of information (each worth one mark). Some of these must require the labelling of chords with Roman numerals (and inversion letters if necessary). Note that a model answer should be given first (e.g. indicate that bar 1 beat 1 = chord I), partly to help identify the key.

➢ Other questions can involve recognising types of non-chord note (e.g. passing notes, suspensions or anticipations), cadences or keys. Check on the expected 'harmonic and tonal vocabulary' in the specification (page 58, section 4).

➢ It is not always necessary to go to the trouble of inventing whole analysis questions or working with music on three staves. It is always useful to practise identifying keys, chords, cadences and non-chord notes in hymn tunes and chorales (or indeed in any type of music).

Practice material for the SATB harmony question

Phrases from hymn tunes and chorales can provide useful practice. Copy out the whole melody for your students, together with the alto, tenor and bass parts for all but the final five beats of the melody. Students must then supply the missing parts, beginning with the bass part.

If hymn tunes are used, it's best to work with those composed in the 18th and 19th centuries. Avoid choosing phrases that appear to have chromatic notes, or that modulate. Often the first or the last phrase of a hymn will be most suitable for Unit 3 practice.

If phrases from chorales are chosen, students are not obliged to reproduce the characteristics of Bach's often rather elaborate style of harmonisation – something simpler will be perfectly acceptable.

Answers and how to mark them

Note that in the following mark schemes, letters, words or phrases in brackets are not essential: for example 'oboe(s)' means that you get the mark for 'oboe' or for 'oboes'. Numbers in brackets are numbers of marks to be awarded. An oblique stroke (/) separates alternative correct solutions. Letters, words or phrases which are <u>underlined</u> are essential: you don't get the mark without them. If you ever provide *correct and relevant* information that is not listed below – for no mark scheme is completely comprehensive – you may receive credit for this. Ask your teacher if in doubt.

Section A (Listening)

2014 Test 1

Based on Edexcel Anthology No. 2, bars 1–44.

(a) oboe(s) (1). NB: *not* violins, who play an octave lower, and have a syncopated rhythm in bar 1.

(b)

or

one mark per ornament – don't accept acciaccatura (♪) or trill not on minim F.

(c) (minim) appoggiatura (E) (1). NB: *not* suspension: the dissonance is not prepared.

(d) a decorated version of the printed melody (1), involving continuous (1) quavers/shorter notes (1); broken chords/arpeggiated (1) with repeated Fs/notes making a (tonic) pedal (1). Max. (3).

(e) conjunct/stepwise (1); 3rds/10ths (above bass/printed part) (1); <u>begins with</u> different rhythm/crotchet and two quavers (1); E♭ suggests B♭ major/secondary dominant/V⁽⁷⁾ of IV/modal inflection (because melody is based on plainsong) (1). Max. (2).

(f) F major (1); perfect (1).

(g) strings <u>plus</u> woodwind/oboes and bassoons (1) without horns (1) (plus) harpsichord (1); octaves (1 – *not* 'unison'); followed by (two) (block) chords/homophony (1). Max. (3).

(h) B (1).

(i) A (1).

2014 Test 2

Based on Edexcel Anthology No. 31, bars 7–26.

(a) (double) octaves (1). NB: in an analytical context, 'unison' is too inexact, even though when men and women sing the same tune in octaves (as sometimes in church services) this is informally referred to as 'unison'.

(b) <u>minor</u> 3rd (1).

(c) cello(s) (1); (double) bass(es) (1).

(d) tenor(s) (1); bass(es) (1); octave (1).

(e) A (1).

(f) ostinato (1).

(g) augmented 4th/tritone (1), Accept instead 'diminished 5th'.

(h) <u>major</u> 3rd(s)/chord (1) without 5th (1), but with minor/dominant 7th (above bass/root) (1). Max. (2).

(i) bassoon(s) (1); horn(s) (1).

(j) (double) bass(es) (1); pizzicato (1). In an exam, you *may* get the second mark for writing 'plucked', but it is wiser to use the standard term 'pizzicato'.

2014 Test 3

Based on Edexcel Anthology No. 18, bars 1–67.

(a) cello (1); pizzicato (1).

(b) imitation (1) (one beat) later (1), a (diminished, then perfect) 5th below (1); piano in octaves (as violin and viola are) (1). Max. (2).

(c) homophonic (1); double-stopping (in violin I) (1).

(d) major key (instead of minor) (1); same melodic outline (1), different rhythm and/or metre (1). Max. (2).

(e) descending sequence (1).

(f) string octaves (1: not unison); imitation (1) (of string melody by piano) (in a) higher (octave) (1); (block) chords/chordal accompaniment (in piano) (1). Max. (3).

(g) G minor (1); imperfect (1).

(h) A (1).

(i) A (1).

2014 Test 4

Based on Edexcel Anthology No. 55, bars 35–end.

(a) bass (1) with (baritone/tenor) sax(ophone)(s) (1); brass/(two) trumpets (1). Max. (2).

(b) syncopation (1); back-beat (1); triplets (1). Max. (2).

(c) same as in bars 2–5 (1); one chord per bar (in bars 6–8) (1), then (much) faster harmonic rhythm/rate of chord change/more chords in bar 9 (1); more adventurous harmony than elsewhere in the piece (1); non-functional (1); chords descending in whole tones (in bar 9) (1); parallel (1) root-position (1) chords. Max. (3).

(d) G♭ (1); D♭ (1); A♭ (1).

(e) stepwise (and/or repeated-note) backing vocals (1); leaps in lead vocals (1) outlining an octave/arpeggio/broken chord (1); lead vocals (heavily) syncopated (1); backing vocals begin on the second beat of the bar (1); syllabic (1) except briefly in lead vocals (1). Max. (3).

(f) homophonic (1).

(g) C (1).

(h) C (1).

2014 Test 5

Based on Edexcel Anthology No. 24, bars 9–28.

(a) homophonic (1) in many/five/six parts (1); chords moving in parallel (1); root-position triads/$\frac{5}{3}$s (at first) (1); later (parallel) 7th chords (1); harmonic rhythm faster from bar 3 (in quavers not crotchets) (1). Max. (4).

(b) it is (exactly) the same (1).

(c) triplet quavers (1).

(d) begins with two quavers (instead of a crotchet)/passing note(s) added (1).

(e) melody same (1) but three octaves lower/at a (much) lower octave (1); melody doubled in octaves (both times) (1); bar 11 has (spread) chords (1); bar 12 unaccompanied octaves (1). Max. (4).

(f) chords based on 'piles of 4ths'/4ths superimposed vertically (1) which sometimes move in parallel (1); chromatic passing notes at ends of bars (15, 17, 19) (1); the chord heard at bar 15, beat 1/the first chord is heard repeatedly (1); harmonic sequence (bars 17–18 and 19–20) (1). Max. (3).

(g) syncopation (1). NB: you can see the syncopated minim from the skeleton score; but note also the crotchet in the left hand which begins on the second half of beat 2.

(h) D (1).

2014 Test 6

Based on Edexcel Anthology No. 34, bars 1–43.

(a) imitation (at the unison) (1).

(b) (perfect) 5th (1).

(c) hemiola (1).

(d) D (major) (1).

(e) canon/imitation (1) at the unison (1) at one beat's distance/one beat behind (1). Max. (2).

(f)   homophonic/chordal/homorhythmic (1).

(g)   dialogue (1) between two (1) pairs of parts (1) at the same pitch (1), while the other/middle/fifth part has a narrowly-moving (1) cantus-firmus-like part (1). Accept instead reference to imitation (1) at the unison (1). Max. (4).

(h)   (G major) IV/C major chord (1); (G major) V/D major chord (1); (G major) I/G major chord (1).

(i)   B (1).

(j)   A (1).

2014 Test 7

Based on Edexcel Anthology No. 2, bars 45–87.

(a)   F major (1); G minor (1).

(b)   circle of 5ths (2)/sequence (1).

(c)   oboes (1).

(d)   diminished 7th (1). NB: *not* just 'diminished' or 'diminished triad'.

(e)   A minor (1); Ic (1); V (1), but accept V⁷.

(f)   strings <u>plus</u> woodwind/oboes and bassoons (with harpsichord), (1) plus horns <u>at the start</u> (1); violins <u>in unison</u> (1); lower strings (including violas) in <u>octaves</u> (1) doubled by bassoons (1); oboes double violin <u>an octave higher</u> (1); basically a two-part texture (1). Max. (3).

(g)   D minor (1); perfect (1).

(h)   C (1).

(i)   B (1).

2014 Test 8

Based on Edexcel Anthology No. 51, bars 37–26 (repeat).

(a)   vocalisation/melismatic (1).

(b)   <u>lead</u> guitar (1).

(c)

(d)   harmonica (1).

(e)   slide (1); chords (1).

(f)   vocal has melody (1); instruments accompany (1), with chords on strong beats (of bars 15–17) (1) and fills (1) in lead guitar and/or drums (1). Max. (3).

(g)   C⁹ (1), but accept C⁷; G⁷ (1); D⁷ (1).

(h)   swung/shuffle (1).

(i)   B (1).

(j)   C (1).

2014 Test 9

Based on Edexcel Anthology No. 18, bars 67–116.

(a)   C (1).

(b)   minor (1).

(c)   viola (1).

(d)   transfers it to piano (RH) (1) a 4th (1) higher (1) as a fugal answer (1). Max. (2).

(e)   viola (1).

(f)   rising (1) sequence (1).

(g)   (at first) rising (1) sequence (1); repetition (1) (of patterns involving) semitonal movement/semitone rise and fall (1); then repetition of these patterns (a 4th) higher (1). Max. (3).

(h)   homophonic (1). Violin(s) have melody (1); (lower/other) strings have on-the-beat/crotchet chords (1); violin (II) double-stopping (1); piano (RH) has off-beat chords (1); piano (LH) has same rhythm as (violin) melody (1). Max. (3).

(i)   imperfect/Phrygian (1); E♭ (major) (1).

2014 Test 10

Based on Edexcel Anthology No. 31, bars 150–168.

(a)   soprano(s) (1); bass(es) (1).

(b)   canon/imitation/pedal/ostinato (in bass) (1).

(c)   (first) oboe(s) (1).

(d)   melody plus <u>contrapuntal</u> accompaniment (1); <u>soprano</u>/<u>melody</u> rises (1) in minims (1); mixture of tones and semitones (1) above imitation (1) based on theme from bar 1/using dotted rhythms (1). Max. (3).

(e)   homophonic/chordal (1).

(f)   slower (1).

(g)   sopranos move narrowly/have range of a (minor) 3rd (1) with semitonal/chromatic movement near end (C–D♭–D♮ etc.) (1); altos and/or tenors/inner part(s) have very narrow ranges (also) (1); bass has repeated octave leaps (falling and rising from B♭ to B♭) (1); bass doubles soprano (at the octave) <u>near end</u> (1); mostly syllabic/(occasional) short melismas (1). Max. (3).

(h)   (even) minims (1) ostinato (1) of <u>four</u> notes (1) within the <u>triple</u>/**3/2** time signature (1) based on (falling and rising) (perfect) 4ths (1)/E♭–B♭–F–B♭ (1). Max. (3).

(i)

2015 Test 1

Based on Edexcel Anthology No. 1, bars 1–59.

(a)   (first) recorder/flute (1).

(b)   I (1); V (1); I (1).

(c)   (harmonic) sequence (1).

(d)   D (major) (1); dominant (1).

(e)   all strings <u>at first</u> (plus harpsichord) (1); cellos and basses silent (later) (1); recorders/flutes <u>at first</u> (1); parallel 6ths in (ripieno) violins (1); <u>solo violin</u> pedal/sustained low note (A) (1); homophonic (1). Max. (3).

(f)   C (1).

(g)   C (major) (1); subdominant (1).

(h)   sequence (1); syncopation (in recorders) (1); suspensions (1). Max. (2).

(i)   C (1).

2015 Test 2

Based on Edexcel Anthology No. 35, bars 1–29.

(a)   homophony (1) in three parts (1).

(b)   transposed (1), up (1) a 3rd (1)/in B♭ (major) (1) instead of G minor (1); with a (stronger) tritonal/augmented 4th dissonance between the outer parts (1). Max. (3).

(c)   imperfect (1).

(d)   a 3rd (1) higher (1), with a diminished 5th (instead of a perfect 5th) (1); sung by a different part (canto not quinto) (1). Max. (2).

(e)   B (1).

(f)   D minor (1); perfect (1); tierce de Picardie (1).

(g)   homophonic/homorhythmic/chordal (1); three parts (1).

(h)   bar 8 (1).

(i)   B (1).

2015 Test 3

Based on Edexcel Anthology No. 9, bars 1–27.

(a)   C (1).

(b)   viola (1); (second) violin (1); (first) violin (1).

(c)   imitation (1). Accept instead 'fugal', because the textural build-up from one to four parts is similar to what happens at the start of many fugues.

(d) double (1) octaves (1) plus (viola) pedal (1). Max. (2). NB: 'double octaves' involve simultaneous use of three notes of the same pitch class (e.g. three Cs) with two whole octaves separating the highest from the lowest.

(e) chromatic (1).

(f) suspension (1). NB: unusually the suspension at the beginning of bar 20 moves chromatically to another dissonance before resolving on beat 3.

(g) sequence (1).

(h) homophonic/chordal (1).

(i) diatonic (1), (beginning with) chord V (1); (then) Ib (1); (then) IV (1); (ending with a) perfect cadence (1); (chord V has a 9-8) suspension (1); no 3rd <u>in the final chord</u> (1). Max. (4).

(j) Symphony No.1 (1). NB: there is a quotation from the fifth symphony later in the movement – not 'in this excerpt'.

2015 Test 4

Based on Edexcel Anthology No. 39, bars 1–28.

(a) a three-note chord (1) I (1) in root position (1) is <u>repeated throughout</u> (1) in the right hand (1) as an introduction (1). Max. (2).

(b) (part of) a circle of 5ths (1) with 7th chords (1) and 9th chords/suspensions and/or appoggiaturas (1); secondary dominant(s) (e.g. bar 5, with D♭) (1); modal inflection(s) (bar 3, with A♮) (1); false relation (B♭ and B♮ in bar 7) (1); augmented triad (bar 6) (1); harmonic rhythm irregular/begins with dotted minims, then changes (1). Max. (4).

(c) minor (1) 6th (1).

(d) E♭ (major) (1); perfect (1).

(e) C minor (1); V⁷ (1).

(f) ascending (1) stepwise/conjunct (1); notes 5–8 of <u>harmonic</u> minor scale/C–D♭–E♮–F/with augmented 2nd (1). Max. (2).

(g)

(h) C (1).

2015 Test 5

Based on Edexcel Anthology No. 19, bars 1–25.

(a) trumpet (in C) (1).

(b) G (major) (1); perfect (1).

(c) in bars 5–6: trumpet rhythm changed/no semiquavers (1); horn's quaver patterns different (some reversed) (1); horn's C♯ was originally C♮ (1); trombone has <u>minims</u>/minim Gs (1) (instead of crotchet Gs in bars 1–2); there is a (fourth) minim G (instead of the C in bar 2) (1), with (chord IV in G being changed to) V⁷(d) in D (1). Max. (4).

(d) D (major) (1).

(e) faster (1).

(f) octave (1) lower (1); louder (1); more staccato notes (1); ends differently (1) without semiquavers (1). Max. (3).

(g) fragmented/shared between (the three) instruments (1); descending triad shape (1) heard in various rhythms/with augmentation in trombone (1); first major <u>then minor</u> (1). Max. (2).

(h) D (1).

(i) C (1).

2015 Test 6

Based on Edexcel Anthology No. 56, bars 1–20.

(a) flute (1).

(b) B (1).

(c) lead vocal has melody (1); instruments accompany (1), although bass has melodic qualities as well (1); electric guitar fill(s) (1) partly double the bass (1); piano has comping (1); regular on-the-beat drum part (1). Max. (4).

(d) E♭ (1); F (1); B♭ (1).

(e) one phrase (1) not two (1); ends/is mostly higher (1); includes a triplet (1); phrase in bar 16 finishes on dominant (1), bar 14 on tonic (1); bar 15 has (the largest melodic interval) – a (falling) perfect 4th (1). Max. (3).

(f)

(g)   B♭ (major) (1); plagal (1).

(h)   C (1).

2015 Test 7

Based on Edexcel Anthology No. 22, bars 1–31.

(a)

allow quaver appoggiatura, but not acciaccatura (♪).

(b)   melody (1) plus (quaver) broken-chord accompaniment (1)/melody-dominated homophony (1); two parts (1). Max. (2).

(c)   syncopation (1).

(d)   IIb (1), V/Ic–V (1), I (1)/perfect cadence (1); double (1) suspension (at bar 9, beat 3) (1), 9–8 and/or 7–6 (1). Accept, instead of a reference to Ic, double appoggiatura at bar 9 beat 4 (1). No dissonance in bar 10 (1). Max (4).

(e)   accented passing note (1). Such a prominent dissonance can alternatively (and correctly) be described as an appoggiatura, even though it is not approached by a leap.

(f)   imperfect (1); F (major) (1). NB: the cadence ends with a C major chord after a passage containing some B♮s. However this is not the key of C major (unlikely in a Classical-period piece that begins in B♭ major) but F major, in readiness for the second subject at bar 23, with some *chromatic* B♮s.

(g)   homophonic (1).

(h)   (harmonic) sequence (1).

(i)   bar 31: the chord at beat 1 has fewer parts/is less dense (1); extra bass note on beat 2 (1). Max. (1).

(j)   B (1).

(k)   B (1).

2015 Test 8

Based on Edexcel Anthology No. 53, bars 25 (repeat)–60.

(a)   (melody-dominated) homophony/melody and accompaniment (1).

(b)   heterophony/follows same melodic shape (1) but with different rhythm (1); octave higher (1). Max. (2).

(c)   two parts (1); upper/one has long notes (1) and includes a rising major 9th (1); lower/the other is (partly) syncopated (1), beginning with quavers (1). Max. (2).

(d)   has (two) short fragments/long rests (1) instead of continuous movement (1); second fragment is considerably higher (1). Max. (2).

(e)   B^7 (1); A (1).

(f)   electric guitar/lead guitar (1).

(g)   dominant 7th/chord V^7/B^7 (1) throughout (1).

(h)   stepwise/conjunct (1), rising then falling (1); moves from lead vocal (1) to one of the backing vocal parts (1), then the other (1). The first two statements are at the same pitch (1), the third a 3rd higher (1). Syncopation (1). Max. (3).

(i)   B (1).

2015 Test 9

Based on Edexcel Anthology No. 1, bars 185–235.

(a)   A minor (1).

(b)   continuous (1) demisemiquavers (1).

(c)   V$^{(7)}$ (1); I (1).

(d)   canon/imitation (1) at the unison (1) at one beat's/quaver's distance (1). Max. (2).

(e)   C (major) (1).

(f)   all instruments/all soloists plus strings plus harpsichord (1); double-/triple-stopping (in solo violin) (1) (mostly) in 6ths (1); (dominant) pedal (in upper strings) (1); lower strings and/or recorders have detached quavers (at beginning of each bar) (1); recorders move in parallel/have same rhythm (1); homophonic (1). Max. (4).

(g) circle of 5ths/sequence (1).

(h) hemiola (1).

(i) perfect (1).

(j) C (1).

2015 Test 10

Based on Edexcel Anthology No. 32, bars 1–7.

(a) bar 1 is monophonic (1); bar 2 is two-part (1) and homorhythmic/homophonic/counterpoint of two rhythmically identical melodies (1).

(b) G (major) (1).

(c) B (1).

(d) exactly the same (1) (apart from different words).

(e) retrograde/backwards (1).

(f) third/sixth (quaver: F♮ and A) (1).

(g) 'bright' (1).

(h) homophonic/homorhythmic/chordal (1) in four parts (1).

(i) suspension (1) *or* 9–8 (suspension) (1); perfect (1); E modal (1) minor (1).

(j) A (1).

2015 Test 11

Based on Edexcel Anthology No. 9, bars 79–104.

(a) homophonic/homorhythmic/chordal (1).

(b) E♭ (1) minor (1).

(c) C minor (1); perfect (1).

(d) B (1).

(e) same rhythm (1); bars 9–11 descend (1) chromatically/in semitones (1) throughout (1); bars 12–14 ascend (1) <u>partly</u> chromatically/in semitones (1), but later have (three) leaps (1). Max. (4).

(f) minor (1); C (1); major (1).

(g) A (1); C (1).

(h) C (1).

2015 Test 12

Based on Edexcel Anthology No. 35, bars 39–67.

(a) same rhythm (1); a 3rd (1) lower (1) except <u>at one point</u> where it is a 4th lower (1). Max. (2).

(b) G minor (1).

(c) <u>begins</u> with repeated chords (of B♭ major) (1); parallel (1) $\frac{6}{3}$/first-inversion triads (1), with false relations (1); two-chord (1) sequential (1) pattern. Max (4).

(d) (tonic) pedal (1).

(e) five-part (1) homophonic/homorhythmic/chordal (1).

(f) three (1).

(g) chords IIIb (1) to I (1)/a variant/distorted perfect cadence (1). Tierce de Picardie in the final chord (1). Max. (2).

(h) repetition of 'Ohimè' arising from 'thousands' in the text (1); minor mode (1); dissonances (portray the singers' mock agony) (1); if not previously mentioned, false relations (1). Max. (2).

(i) C (1).

2015 Test 13

Based on Edexcel Anthology No. 19, bars 34–56.

(a) (even/all) crotchets (1).

(b) (at first) leaps (up and down) two octaves (1), getting louder/***f***, ***ff***, ***fff*** (1), then (long/big) scalic (1) descent (1) (mostly) in semiquavers (1), with some chromatic movement/E♮–E♭ (1). Max. (3).

(c) B♭ (major) (1); V/V⁷ (1).

(d) homophonic (1); (all notes) staccato (1); trombone and trumpet alternate (1) together with a (more-or-less) continuous part for horn (1) making a two-part texture (1). Max. (3).

(e) perfect (1); F (major) (1).

(f) second phrase: ends with a scalic run (down) (1) from C (1); articulation is different (1). Max. (2).

(g) trumpet run is different (1) – C Db Eb F Gb/(mostly) a semitone lower (1); dynamics and/or articulation different (1); repeated chords different (1) implying different 7th chords (1). Max. (2).

(h) B (1).

2015 Test 14

Based on Edexcel Anthology No. 56, bars 21–36.

(a) sax(ophone) (1).

(b) three-part (1) counterpoint/contrapuntal (1), which is free/non-imitative (1) except that acoustic guitar echoes sax <u>at the beginning</u> (1), (above) bass, which outlines the harmonies (1); electric guitar is generally the highest (1) and most melodic part (1). Max. (4).

(c)

accept instead notes written an octave lower.

(d) syncopation (1); alternates (1) between two notes/F and D (1). Max. (2).

(e) electric guitar <u>begins with</u> (four) quavers (1) but has (mainly) (groups of four) semiquavers (1); acoustic guitar has (mainly) triplet (quavers) (1). Max. (2).

(f) Dm (1); Eb (1); Bb (1).

(g) B (1).

2015 Test 15

Based on Edexcel Anthology No. 22, bars 63[4]–97.

(a) sequence (1).

(b) diminished 7th (1); second (1); V (1); perfect (1).

(c) F minor (1).

(d) melody (1) plus Alberti bass (1)/(melody-dominated) homophony (1); two-part (1). Max. (2).

(e) syncopation (1).

(f) G minor (1); imperfect (1).

(g) less frequently (1). NB: the prolonged dominant harmony (chord V, V[7] and V with a flattened 9th) helps to prepare the listener for the approach of the recapitulation, with the return of the probably well-remembered opening theme. Prolonged use of chord V is a favourite Classical way of saying to the listener: 'Wait for it … something very important is about to happen!'

(h) Bb major (1); appoggiatura (1); (upward-resolving) suspension and appoggiatura (1), but accept instead double suspension/double appoggiatura.

(i) C (1).

2015 Test 16

Based on Edexcel Anthology No. 63, bars 1–24.

(a) cuatro (1).

(b) monophonic (1).

(c) F#dim[7]/diminished 7th chord (on F#) (1); Gm/G minor triad (in root position)/chord I (1).

(d) (double) bass (1); claves (1); maracas (1).

(e) bongo(s) (1).

(f) D[7] (1); Gm (1).

(g) first note is Bb/3rd lower (than bar 13) (1); third note is Bb/4th lower (1).

(h) (Mostly) two-part (1) with same rhythm in both parts (1); some <u>parallel</u> 3rds (1); some contrary motion (1). Max. (2).

(i) D (1).

(j) C (1).

Section C (Understanding Chords and Lines)

Question 4

In questions which require Roman numerals, inverted chords may be referred to by using inversion letters (b, as in Ib; c, as in Ic; or d, as in V⁷d), or figured-bass notation may be used (e.g. I6 instead of Ib, I$_4^6$ instead of Ic, V$_2^4$ instead of V⁷d). In the mark schemes below, we have given inversion letters; ask your teacher for help if you need to have these translated into figured-bass notation. Marks are not awarded for popular-music-style chord symbols (G, Em⁷, D/F♯ and so on): the questions ask specifically for Roman numerals.

Test 1

Source: Beethoven, 'Oh care selve', WoO 119, bars 5–16 (transposed from G major to F major).

(a) (F major) V⁷ (1: award the mark only if both the V and the ⁷ are given); VI (1); IIb (1: award the mark only if both the II and the b are given); V (1): yes, plain V this time.

(b) Ib (1); V⁷ (1). Concerning the Ib: note that the bass in bar 6 is arpeggiated (A–C–F–A), and that it is sensible to think of chord Ib *as lasting for five quaver beats* – it is pointless to say that there is movement here from Ib to Ic to I and back to Ib! Notice also that when the chord begins it consists of As and Cs only – the F comes in on the 3rd quaver. In view of the clear emphasis on F major harmony in bar 6, it would be wrong to say that the As and Cs at the start of bar 6 are part of chord III without an E.

(c) B (1).

(d) D (1).

Answers to additional practice questions: (i) bar 5: IIb, V; bar 6 (end): IIb; bar 7 begins with Ic; bars 8–9: I; bar 10: Ic–V. (ii) C major. (iii) C major V⁷, I. (iv) both perfect.

Test 2

Source: Beethoven, 'Gesang aus der Ferne', WoO 137, bars 24–31.

(a) (B♭ major) V⁷ (1); I (1); II⁷b (1); Ic (1); IVb (1).

(b) (lower) auxiliary note (1).

(c) B (1).

(d) imperfect (1).

Answers to additional practice questions: (i) bar 6: Ic (on last quaver); bar 7: IIb, II (4th quaver), (passing notes on 5th quaver), IIb implied (last quaver); bar 8: Ic, V. (ii) bars 1 and 3: the ornaments (appoggiaturas) are appoggiaturas in terms of harmonic analysis also; bar 3: B♭ is an auxiliary note; bar 6: F is an appoggiatura; bar 7: Fs (3rd quaver) are passing notes, all notes on the 5th quaver are passing notes. (iii) perfect.

Test 3

Source: 'Dafydd y garreg wen'/'David of the white rock' (traditional Welsh melody), part of verse 2, words given in English. Specially arranged for this volume.

(a) imperfect (1) E minor (1).

(b) interrupted (1).

(c) diminished 7th (chord) (1). If asked for 'type' of chord, it is *likely* that the answer will be 'diminished 7th chord' *or* 'diminished chord in 1st inversion'.

(d) (G major) IV (1); V⁷ (without 5th) (1); IVb (1); VI (1).

Answers to additional practice questions: (i) bar 1: E minor I, IIb; bar 2: Ic, V; bar 3: I, Ib, IIb; bar 4: Ic, V, VI; bar 6: V (with suspension), V⁷ (beat 3); bar 7, beats 1–2: IVb (with some non-harmonic notes); beat 3: IIb; bar 8: Ib, VIIb, I; bar 9: Vb, V; bar 10: *G major* Ib; bar 12 (beats 2 and 3): IIb, IIIb; bar 13 (beats 2 and 3): II⁷b, V; bar 14: I; bar 15: VI = *E minor* I, Ib, V⁷; bar 16: I. (ii) Too many to list all, but note in particular bars 1 and 3: quaver A = appoggiatura (accented passing note is an acceptable alternative in view of the stepwise movement within a single chord); bar 7: quaver B = appoggiatura (unusually, on a weak part of the beat); quaver G = passing note; bass crotchet B = passing note involving octave displacement (you might expect it to be an octave lower); bar 13: quaver B = appoggiatura. (iii) B major, imperfect; G major, perfect; E major, perfect. (iv) tierce de Picardie.

Test 4

Source: 'The Golden Vanity' (English folk song), verse 1 and beginning of chorus. Specially arranged for this volume.

(a) VI (1) – yes, VI, because the key is C major; Ib (1); IV (1).

(b) G major (1).

(c) C (1).

(d) F (1).

(e) suspension (1).

(f) diminished (chord) (in 1st inversion) (1).

Test 5

Source: Haydn, 'What art expresses' (also known as 'Dr Harington's Compliment'), Hob. XXVIb:3, bars 1–2 and 7–21 (i.e. with abbreviated introduction).

(a) (A major) Ib (1); IIb (1); VIIb (1); Ic (1).

(b) perfect (1).

(c) diminished 7th (chord) (1).

(d) B minor (1).

(e) D (1).

Test 6

Source: J.W. Franck, *Geistliche Lieder* (1681) (transposed from E minor, and specially edited for this volume).

(a) (F minor) IV (1); Vb/V⁷b (in view of the short B♭ in the vocal part) (1); Ic (1); V (1).

(b) tierce de Picardie (1).

(c) anticipation: A♭, bar 13 (1); échappée: E♭, bar 11/D♭, bar 13 (1).

(d) E♭ major (1).

Test 7

Source: specially-composed setting of a stanza by Andrew Marvell (1621–1678) from 'A Dialogue between the Resolved Soul and Created Pleasure'.

(a) (E major) VI (1); Ib (1); IV (1): the harmony is still IV, despite the appoggiatura D♯ on beat 1 and the passing note F♯ at the end of beat 2. The passing note F♯, together with the A and C♯ below it, momentarily creates a set of notes (A–C♯–F♯) which, if more prolonged, might deserve to be labelled separately as IIb.

(b) E minor (1) (E minor is the tonic minor, easily reached because chord V is the same in both a major key and its tonic minor); C♯ minor (1). Can you see how the journey from E minor to C♯ minor was effected?

(c) suspension (1): a response to the word 'suspend'?

(d) A (1).

(e) plagal (1). Plagal cadences are rare – but they do occur!

Test 8

Source: 18th-century Jacobite song. Specially arranged for this volume.

(a) (C minor) II⁷b (1); V⁷d (1); Ib (1); V⁷c (1).

(b) suspension (1).

(c) E♭ major (1); F minor (1).

(d) A (1).

Test 9

Source: Schubert, 'Heidenröslein', D. 257, bars 1–16.

(a) (G major) V⁷b (1); V⁷(d) (1); Ib (1).

(b) appoggiatura (1). At first glance, the note may seem not to be a non-harmonic (non-chord) note at all – after all, it is a 5th (a consonant interval) above the bass G. But the chord, as we can see from the three notes in the right hand at the second quaver of bar 6, is D major V⁷d (G–E–A–C♯), to which chord the note D does not of course belong.

(c) bars 9–10 end with a perfect cadence/chord I (1) whereas bars 7–8 end with an interrupted cadence/chord VI (1).

(d) perfect cadence (1).

(e) D (1).

Question 5

Note: Marking harmony exercises is far from straightforward – ask your teacher to help you with the marking of these tests.

We haven't given a correct answer to each test, because there will always be several possible correct answers. Where a test is based on a hymn tune or chorale, we've identified this. You might want to compare what you've written with the original, but remember that many hymn tunes appear in slightly different versions (and different keys) in different hymn books, and that the original harmonisation may not be the only one possible. Where no source for an exercise is given, the music has been specially composed.

We have provided general marking guidance below, which can be applied to all of the tests. But we have also made one or two particular recommendations for each test.

For each test, 12 marks are available.

For choosing appropriate chords and for correct part-writing: 10 marks are available.

Give two marks for each chord that has been chosen appropriately and is correct in terms of part-writing (that is, without consecutive 5ths and other such faults).

Give one mark where:

➢ A chord is an unsuitable choice, but is not totally wrong. For example, imagine that someone wrote, in C major, chords III–I at the end of a phrase, under the notes B and C. The chord III would be unsuitable, because there's no such cadence as III–I. But if the part-writing connected with the III–I progression were correct, 1 mark could still be awarded for the chord III (and 2 marks for the chord I).

➢ A chord contains one obviously wrong note (e.g. in C–E–F–C the F makes no sense – the writer clearly meant, but did not succeed in writing, a C major chord with C–E–G–C).

➢ A chord has one note missing.

➢ A chord has one part-writing problem, which probably means that this chord:

    ➢ Marks the end of a single set of consecutive 5ths or octaves

    ➢ Actually contains within it a single set of consecutive 5ths or octaves

    ➢ Has a doubling of the leading note

    ➢ Has some other problem with doubling (e.g. a root-position chord has no 3rd – C–C–G–C with no E)

    ➢ Has unsuitable spacing (notably with more than an octave between neighbouring upper parts)

    ➢ Has parts that cross for no good reason

    ➢ Has parts that overlap for no good reason

    ➢ Stands at the end of an unsuitable melodic interval (probably an augmented 2nd or 4th).

Give no mark where a chord:

➢ Is unsuitable *and* there is one part-writing problem.

➢ Has two part-writing problems.

➢ Has two obviously wrong notes.

➢ Has two notes missing.

For special features: 2 marks are available.

Give one mark for each special feature correctly used.

Special features are mainly appropriate non-harmonic notes (otherwise called 'non-chord' notes) such as passing notes and suspensions, but you could also gain a mark for including a tierce de Picardie as part of a perfect cadence at the end of an exercise in a minor key.

See the next page for specific marking guidance on each of the Question 5 tests.

Test 1

Source: hymn tune 'St Flavian' (derived from Day's *Psalter*, 1562). This tune, as given in, for example, *The New English Hymnal* (The Canterbury Press Norwich, 1986), no. 147, has contrary-motion consecutive octaves between soprano and bass at the last two chords (I and Ib) of bar 1. This is better avoided in your own work: chords I and VI will work well, and you can also use a passing note E in the bass.

Marking guidance: F major: end with a perfect cadence. You *could* write an interrupted cadence, but remember that few phrases in simple styles of music end with interrupted cadences, whereas perfect cadences are a standard feature. At bar 2, beats 1–2, you could write V twice in a row, but this is dull unless a 4–3 suspension sounds on beat 1 (compare bar 1, beats 1–2). Bar 2 could well begin with IIb, II⁷b, or even plain II, to lead on to V at beat 2.

Test 2

Source: hymn tune 'Eudoxia', S. Baring-Gould (1834–1924).

Marking guidance: G major: end with a perfect cadence. The approach chord could be II, IIb, or II⁷b (as in the original).

Test 3

Source: melody adapted from J. Regnart (1574): see *The Chorale Book for England* (1863). Harmony from *Songs of Praise* (OUP, 1931), no. 109 (transposed from E minor to G minor).

Marking guidance: G minor: end with an imperfect cadence, approached from I or Ib (not VI, which would give consecutive 5ths between soprano and bass). The harmonisation in the source cited above keeps entirely to the *harmonic* minor scale: this is safest, but the composer might well have put in a passing note F♮ (from the descending *melodic* minor scale) in the bass of bar 1 (between the G and E♭).

Test 4

Marking guidance: D minor: end with an perfect cadence. One possible answer could be V, VI, IV, V, I (perhaps with a tierce de Picardie).

Test 5

Source: hymn tune 'St Stephen', W. Jones (1726–1800).

Marking guidance: A major: end with a perfect cadence. In the original, the last three notes of the melody, with notes 3–2–1 of the scale, are harmonised as Ic–V–I.

Test 6

Source: hymn tune 'Melcombe', S. Webbe (1740–1816).

Marking guidance: E♭ major. The original ends with IV–I (a plagal cadence); an imperfect cadence is possible, perhaps IIb–V. The first chord you add will almost certainly be I (the given alto D rising to E♭).

Test 7

Marking guidance: A minor: end with a perfect cadence. The approach chord could be IIb or II⁷b. The first chord of bar 2 must have F in the bass (after the G♯ passing note): given the D in the melody, this chord must be IVb. The C and A are likely to belong to I (A–C–E) rather than VI (F–A–C); Ib with C in the bass works better than plain I, which appears twice in bar 1 and throughout bar 3.

Test 8

Source: hymn tune 'Jackson', T. Jackson (1715–1781).

Marking guidance: D major: end with a perfect cadence. Chord V fits with the dotted crotchet A (the G is a passing note), and I with the F♯ (the 3rd of the chord).

Test 9

Source: melody (only) from the hymn tune 'Windsor' (from T. Este's *Psalter*, 1592).

Marking guidance: F♯ minor: end with an imperfect cadence, probably with I or Ib before the final V. Chord IVb would work here instead, though, as would VI if you are able to avoid consecutives.

Test 10

Marking guidance: B minor. The two F♯s at the end (note 5 of the B minor scale) could be harmonised with a perfect cadence (V–I) or with an imperfect (probably I–V). Such ambiguity would be unusual in a Unit 3 harmonisation test, but can't be ruled out. One effective harmonisation for this test would be V (under the A♯), Ib, IV, V, I (with a tierce de Picardie).

Test 11

Source: melody (only) from *Bach Riemenschneider*, no. 164.

Marking guidance: B♭ major: end with a perfect cadence. A 4–3 suspension will work well with chord V under the minim C (crotchet B♭ resolving to crotchet A, if you prepare it). The first chord in bar 2 must be IIb (following the quaver F passing note) in bar 1.

Test 12

Marking guidance: E minor: end with an imperfect cadence. Chords IVb–V, a Phrygian cadence, will work best; indeed, if the melody ends with notes 4–5 of a minor scale, it is usually safe to assume that the cadence is Phrygian. Notes 3–4–5 in a minor key usually support the chords I–IVb–V: often you can put a passing note (the unsharpened 7th of the key) in the bass between I and IVb.

Test 13

Marking guidance: C minor: end with a perfect cadence. The penultimate note in the soprano is an anticipation. One effective harmonic scheme for this test would be Ib (inevitable after the bass' passing note F), VI, Ic (under the minim E♭), V, I (perhaps with a tierce de Picardie).

Test 14

Source: melody (only) from *Bach Riemenschneider*, no. 40.

Marking guidance: C major. The most probable ending where the melody ends with notes 6–7–8 is IV–VIIb–I: VIIb–I is a kind of substitute perfect cadence, suitable for an intermediate phrase ending rather than for the final cadence of an extended piece. II–V–I is possible instead of IV–VIIb–I. It's difficult to use IV–V–I without incurring consecutives.

Test 15

Marking guidance: F major: end with a plagal cadence (the only possible cadence with notes 1–1). In bar 3, V–VI will work well (V–I is less interesting, in view of the impending IV–I, and the likelihood of there being yet another I at the end of bar 2).

Test 16

Marking guidance: E minor: end with a perfect cadence (or with an interrupted?). The leading-note D♯ in the bass of bar 2 leads inevitably to E (chord I). If we end with I, this will be the fourth I in root position in a piece with nine chords! So there could be a case here, very unusually, for having an interrupted cadence, just for the sake of variety.

Glossary

This glossary is not comprehensive: it refers to terms as used in this volume. For more information about harmonic terms (e.g. suspension), see the AS Music Harmony Workbook *and/or the* A2 Music Harmony Workbook *by Hugh Benham (Rhinegold Education, 2008). For fuller definitions of other terms and expressions, consult the* Dictionary of Music in Sound *by David Bowman (Rhinegold Education, 2002).*

Acciaccatura. A very short ornamental note played before a principal melodic note, written as ♪.

Accidental. A symbol that changes the pitch of a note, usually by a semitone.

Alberti bass. A particular type of **broken-chord** pattern often found in Classical keyboard music, with three pitches heard in the order low–high–middle–high (E.g. C–G–E–G).

Anthem. A type of church music for choir, often accompanied by organ, and occasionally by larger forces. An anthem usually has English words (often from the Bible).

Anticipation. A melody note (frequently the tonic of the key in the highest part) sounded slightly before the chord to which it belongs, thereby creating a dissonance with the previous chord.

Antiphony. Performance by different singers/instrumentalists in alternation. Often – but not always – the different groups perform similar material.

Appoggiatura. A **non-chord** note that sounds on the beat and then resolves by step (up or down a semitone or tone) to the main chord note. The dissonant note is not 'prepared' as a **suspension** is. Although appoggiaturas are normally approached by leap, accented **passing notes** that are particularly long and/ or prominent are often described as appoggiaturas, even though they are approached by step.

Articulation. Concerns the degree to which notes are separated from those around them. For example, in a legato performance the progression from one note to the next is as smooth as possible, while staccato notes are clearly detached.

Atonal. Music that avoids keys or modes; that is, no pitch stands out consistently in the way the tonic does in tonal music.

Augmented interval. An augmented interval is one semitone larger than a major or perfect interval: for example, an augmented 4th (C–F♯) is one semitone larger than a perfect 4th (C–F).

Auxiliary note. A **non-chord** note that occurs between, and is a tone or semitone above or below, two harmony notes of the same pitch.

Back-beat. In pop and rock music, syncopated accents on the second and fourth beats of a $\frac{4}{4}$ bar.

Ballett. A lighter type of **madrigal** (a form of secular vocal music cultivated in Italy and England in the 16th and early 17th centuries), with fa-la refrains and a generally syllabic setting.

Baroque. Refers to music written between about 1600 and 1750.

Binary form. A type of musical structure with two sections, each usually repeated (i.e. AABB).

Bitonal. Music that uses two different keys simultaneously.

Blue note. A note (usually the third, fifth or seventh degree of a major scale) performed at a slightly lower pitch than normal for expressive effect.

Bridge. In jazz and pop music, a short, contrasting passage that connects two longer sections.

Broken chord. The performing of the notes of a chord one after another instead of simultaneously.

Cadence. A pair of chords signifying the end of a phrase in tonal music. Cadences are of several types, of which perfect and imperfect are by far the most common. *See also* **Imperfect cadence**, **Interrupted cadence**, **Perfect cadence**, **Plagal cadence** and **Phrygian cadence**.

Calypso. A genre of song from Trinidad characterised by humorous or subversive lyrics. The music itself merges European and African elements.

Canon. A strict form of **imitation**, often lasting for a substantial passage or entire piece, where the second part is an exact (or almost exact) copy of the first, even if at a different pitch.

Cantata. Usually a work for voice(s) and instruments in several movements. A cantata is generally shorter than an oratorio, sometimes without a chorus, and can be sacred or secular.

Chorale. A German hymn of the kind sung in the Lutheran (Protestant) church in the time of Bach. The word 'chorale' can refer to the words only, or the associated melody only, or to the whole hymn. Chorale melodies are largely **conjunct**: their harmonisation has long featured in advanced music courses.

Chordal. A form of **homophony** in which all the parts move together in the same or very similar rhythm. The term homorhythmic (literally 'same rhythm') is sometimes used instead.

Chromatic. A chromatic note is one that does not belong to the scale of the key currently in use. For example, in D major the notes G♯ and C♮ are chromatic. A passage of music containing many chromatic notes may be described as chromatic.

Circle of 5ths. A harmonic progression in which the roots of the chords move by descending 5ths (and/or ascending 4ths), for example B–E–A–D–G–C, etc.

Classical. Refers to music written between about 1750 and 1820.

Claves. A pair of short wooden sticks used to play the clave rhythm in Latin-American styles of music such as son and salsa.

Coda. A concluding section of a movement.

Comping. A term associated with jazz and pop music, referring to the playing of a chordal accompaniment.

Conjunct. Melodic movement by step rather than leap.

Contrapuntal. Adjective to describe music that uses **counterpoint**.

Contrary motion. Movement of two parts in opposite directions (e.g. soprano C–D–E heard at the same time as bass E–D–C).

Counterpoint. Two or more melodic lines (usually rhythmically contrasted), each significant in itself, which are played or sung together at the same time – in contrast to **homophony**, in which one part has the melody and the other parts accompany. The term 'polyphonic' is often used as a synonym for contrapuntal.

Cuatro. A type of Latin-American guitar. It is typically a little smaller than the Western guitar, with just four strings.

Development. The central part of a **sonata-form** movement, placed between the exposition and the recapitulation, and containing the development of ideas already heard in the exposition.

Dialogue. When two or more instruments or voices have a musical 'conversation', with the individual parts responding to one another.

Diatonic. A diatonic note is one that belongs to the scale of the key currently in use. For example, in D major the notes D, E and F♯ are diatonic. A diatonic passage of music just uses notes that belong to the current key.

Diminished interval. An interval that is one semitone narrower than a minor or perfect interval. For example, a diminished 4th (G♯–C) is one semitone narrower than a perfect 4th (G–C).

Diminished 7th chord. A dissonant four-note chord made up of superimposed minor 3rds (for example C♯–E–G–B♭).

Dissonance. Any note not a major or minor 3rd or 6th, perfect 5th, unison or perfect octave above the lowest-sounding part is strictly a dissonance. Triads in root position or in first inversion are therefore the only chords that have no dissonance. Some dissonances, particularly **suspensions** and **appoggiaturas**, add harmonic tension and can help make the music more expressive; others, notably **passing** and **auxiliary** notes, provide rhythmic and melodic decoration.

Dominant 7th. A dissonant four-note chord built on the dominant note of the scale. It includes the dominant triad plus a minor 7th above the root.

Doubled. When a note or passage in one part is played by another part at the same time, either at the same pitch or at a different octave.

Double-stopping. The playing of two note simultaneously on adjacent strings of a string instrument.

Échappée. An échappée (or 'escape note') leaves a harmony note by step (usually upwards) and then leaps in the opposite direction (usually by a 3rd) to a new harmony note.

Exposition. The first section of a **sonata-form** movement, typically including the first subject in the tonic and the second subject in a related key.

False relation. The occurrence of the ordinary and chromatically altered versions of the same note (such as F♯ and F♮) in two different parts at the same time, or in close proximity.

Fill. A short passage of music between two sections of a melody.

Fugal. Adjective to describe music in the style of a **fugue**.

Fugato. A passage in a fugal style that forms part of a larger piece of music.

Fugue. A type of piece in which a main theme (the subject) is treated in **imitation** by all of the parts.

Functional. A type of harmony that has the function of defining a major or minor key, in particular through chords on the tonic and dominant, with a special emphasis on **perfect cadences**.

Galliard. A fast triple-time dance of the **Renaissance** era, usually consisting of three repeated sections (AA,BB,CC).

Harmonic interval. The interval between two notes that are played or sung at the same time.

Harmonic rhythm. The rate at which the harmony changes in a piece.

Hemiola. The articulation of two units of triple time (strong–weak–weak, strong–weak–weak) as three units of duple time (strong–weak, strong–weak, strong–weak).

Heterophony. A texture in which a melody is performed simultaneously with one or more rhythmically and/or melodically varied versions of itself.

Homophony. A texture in which one part has a melody and the other parts accompany, in contrast to **contrapuntal** writing, where each part has independent melodic and rhythmic interest.

Homorhythmic. *See* **Chordal**.

Imitation. When a melodic idea in one part is immediately repeated in another part (exactly or inexactly), at the same or a different pitch, while the first part continues. The adjective is 'imitative'.

Imperfect cadence. An open-ended or inconclusive cadence ending with the dominant chord (V). The preceding chord is usually I, ii or IV.

Instrumentation. The choice of instruments for a piece of music.

Interrupted cadence. A cadence intended to create surprise or suspense, perhaps by delaying the arrival of a final **perfect** or **plagal** cadence. Usually consists of chord V followed by chord VI.

Inversion. When a chord has a note other than the root in the lowest part, it is an inversion. In a first-inversion chord the 3rd of the chord is the lowest part, and in a second-inversion chord the 5th. For example, a triad of F major in first inversion is A–C–F, and in second inversion is C–F–A.

Leading note. The seventh degree of a major or minor scale, usually with a strong tendency to rise to the tonic.

Lied. German for song, but used in English to refer specifically to 19th-century settings of German poetry for an accompanied solo voice.

Madrigal. Usually a secular (non-church) song, often about love in a country setting. Most are for unaccompanied voices.

Melisma. In vocal music, a group of notes sung to a single syllable, often for expressive purposes or word-painting. The adjective is 'melismatic'.

Melodic interval. The interval between two notes that are played or sung one after the other.

Melody-dominated homophony. As with 'ordinary' homophony, a texture in which one part has a melody and the other parts accompany. With melody-dominated homophony, however, the melody stands apart from the accompaniment particularly clearly and strongly.

Metre. Concerns the identity, grouping and subdivision of beats, as indicated by a time signature. E.g. the time signature $\frac{3}{4}$ indicates a simple triple metre, in which each bar consists of three crotchet beats.

Middle eight. In pop music, a contrasting section, often lasting eight bars, that prepares for the return of the main section.

Modal. A term often used to refer to music based on a mode rather than on major or minor keys.

Modulation. A change of key, or the process of changing key.

Monophony. Music consisting only of a single melodic line.

Motet. A type of church music for choir, sometimes accompanied by organ, and occasionally by larger forces. A motet often has Latin words (commonly from the Bible), and is particularly but not exclusively associated with Roman Catholic services.

Motif. A short but distinctive musical idea that is developed in various ways in order to create a longer passage of music.

Neoclassical. A term used for music in which the composer revives elements from an earlier style (not necessarily a Classical one). These elements normally exist alongside more up-to-date ones.

Non-chord note. A note that does not belong to the chord being played. For example, the note B heard against a chord of C major (C–E–G) would be a non-chord (or non-harmony) note.

Opera. A large-scale dramatic work for singers and instrumentalists. In most cases the whole text is sung, so that an opera is very different from a play with incidental music. An opera differs from a musical too in that the music is not generally popular in idiom.

Ostinato. A repeating melodic, harmonic or rhythmic **motif**, heard continuously throughout part or the whole of a piece.

Parallel motion. Movement of two parts in the same direction, with the interval between them remaining essentially the same. Parallel 3rds (usually with a mixture of major and minor 3rds) are common in many styles; parallel perfect 5ths are avoided in some. The opposite of **contrary motion**.

Passing note. A **non-chord note** approached and quitted by a step in the same direction, often filling in a melodic gap of a 3rd (e.g. A between G and B, where G and B are harmony notes).

Pedal note. A sustained or repeated note, usually in a low register, over which changing harmonies occur. A pedal on the fifth note of the scale (a dominant pedal) tends to create a sense of expectation in advance of a perfect cadence; a pedal on the key note (a tonic pedal) can create a feeling of repose.

Pentatonic. A scale made up of five notes, most frequently the first, second, third, fifth and sixth degrees of a major scale (for example, the major pentatonic scale of C is C–D–E–G–A).

Perfect cadence. A cadence ending with the tonic chord (I), preceded by the dominant (V or V^7) – appropriate where some degree of finality is required.

Phrygian cadence. A type of **imperfect** cadence, in which the dominant chord (V) is preceded by the first inversion of the subdominant (IVb). It is used chiefly in minor keys, and particularly in **Baroque** music.

Pizzicato. A direction to pluck, instead of bow, string(s) on a violin, viola, cello or double bass.

Plagal cadence. A cadence ending with the tonic chord (I), preceded by the subdominant (IV).

Prima prattica. A term applied to music of the Renaissance era.

Recapitulation. In a **sonata-form** movement, the section that follows the development. It is often closely based on the exposition, but normally both opens and closes in the tonic key.

Reggae. A genre of popular music originating in Jamaica, with roots in ska and **rocksteady**. It has a distinctive rhythmic style characterised by off-beat accents.

Renaissance. Refers to music written between about 1400 and 1600.

Retrograde. The pitches of a previously heard melody or rhythm presented in reverse order.

Rhythm and blues. A harder-edged form of blues that emerged in American cities in the 1940s.

Ritornello form. A structure used in Baroque music in which an opening instrumental section (called the ritornello) introduces the main musical ideas. This returns, often in a shortened version and in related keys, between passages (episodes) for one or more soloists. The complete ritornello (or a substantial part of it) returns in the tonic key at the end.

Rocksteady. An early form of **reggae**, emerging in the late 1960s.

Romantic. Refers to music written between about 1820 and 1900.

Rondo. A piece in which an opening section in the tonic key is heard several times, with different material (usually in different keys) between these repetitions. The simplest rondo shape is ABACA, but this can be extended.

Root-position chord. A chord which has the root in the lowest-sounding part.

Scherzo. A fast movement that eventually replaced the minuet of the **Classical** era.

Seconda prattica. A term applied to music of the early **Baroque** era, to distinguish it from that of the preceding **Renaissance** style.

Secondary dominant. A passing or temporary dominant hinting at a different key. For example, in C major, an E major chord acting as dominant to a tonic of A minor.

Sequence. Immediate repetition of a melodic or harmonic idea at a different pitch.

Sonata form. Typical first-movement form of the Classical and Romantic periods. In three sections – **exposition**, **development** and **recapitulation** – often based on two groups of melodic material in two contrasting keys (first subject and second subject).

Strophic. A strophic song is one in which each verse has the same (or very similar) music.

Suspension. A suspension occurs at a change of chord, when one part hangs on to (or repeats) a note from the old chord, creating a dissonance, after which the delayed part resolves by step (usually down) to a note of the new chord.

Swung rhythm. In jazz and pop music, a certain freedom in performance whereby rhythms that might be played 'straight' (as equal notes) are performed with the first of each pair longer than the second, often with a kind of **triplet** effect.

Syllabic. The setting of one note to one syllable.

Syncopation. The shifting of stress from a strong to a weak beat. For example, in a $\frac{4}{4}$ bar with the rhythm ♩ 𝅝 ♩, the minim (a relatively long note beginning on a weak beat) is syncopated.

Ternary form. A musical structure of three sections in which the outer sections are similar and the central one is contrasting (ABA).

Texture. The relationship between the various simultaneous lines in a passage of music, dependent on such features as the number and function of the parts and the spacing between them.

Theme and variations. A musical structure in which an initial melodic or harmonic idea is stated (the 'theme), and then developed and varied by the composer (the 'variations').

Through-composed. A song that uses mainly different music for each verse of the text.

Tierce de Picardie. A major 3rd in the final tonic chord of a passage in a minor key.

Tonality. The system of major and minor keys in which one note (the tonic, or key note) has particular importance, and in which various keys are related. For exam purposes, questions on tonality might also include identifying music that is **modal** or that is based on non-Western scales. Western music that uses neither keys nor modes is described as **atonal**.

Trill. An ornament in which two adjacent notes rapidly and repeatedly alternate (the note bearing the trill sign and the one above it). The symbol for a trill is ***tr***.

Tripartite. Meaning 'having three parts', this refers to works in three distinct sections.

Triple-stopping. The playing of three notes simultaneously (or as near simultaneously as possible) on adjacent strings of a string instrument.

Triplet. A group of three equal notes played in the time normally taken by two notes of the same type. For example, a triplet of quavers is played in the time taken by two normal quavers.

Tritone. An interval that is equivalent to three tones (an augmented 4th or diminished 5th).

Turnaround. In jazz and pop music, a short link leading to the next section.

Unison. Simultaneous performance of the same note or melody by two or more players or singers.

Vocalisation. A style of singing in which pitches are produced without distinct words.

Whole-tone scale. A scale in which the interval between every successive note is a whole tone.